# THE MAGIC OF LIFTING WEIGHTS

Rick Newcombe

Creators Publishing
Hermosa Beach, CA

***THE MAGIC OF LIFTING WEIGHTS***


**Cover art by Peter Kaminski**

**CREATORS PUBLISHING**
737 3rd St
Hermosa Beach, CA 90254
310-337-7003

SECOND PRINTING

*Rick Newcombe's email address:* ***rnewcombe@creators.com***



ISBN (print): 978-1-949673-42-5
ISBN (ebook): 978-1-949673-41-8

**First Edition**
Printed in the United States of America
1 3 5 7 9 10 8 6 4 2

# Dedication

To my grandchildren, Scott, Lillian, Warren, and Luca,
who inspire me to stay youthful.

~ ~ ~ ~ ~

# Contents

# THE MAGIC OF LIFTING WEIGHTS

# INTRODUCTION

This is a book about a discovery I made accidentally, which is that lifting weights, with relatively light weights and good form, has helped me to look and feel youthful my whole life.

I am not talking about professional weightlifting or bodybuilding, both of which have been contaminated by chemicals.

Now, I never set out to make this discovery; in fact, it was simply a fortunate byproduct of vanity. I was born in 1950, right in the middle of the baby boomer generation, and I started lifting weights at age twelve to emulate the musclemen on the covers of bodybuilding magazines.

Many other boys and girls had similar aspirations, especially boys who fit the profile of Charles Atlas's "ninety-seven-pound weaklings," who were tired of having sand kicked in their faces. Some achieved success in transforming their bodies. Others did not. I managed to fit into both categories.

I tried and succeeded, but negative self-talk made future success impossible, so I quit and failed. Then, a dozen years later, I tried again, only this time, I succeeded—not as Mr. Universe but as someone who enjoys pumping iron as a hobby and an enjoyable way to stay fit.

As I look back on my experience of lifting weights for more than half a century, I realize that the greatest benefits—good health, a love of life, high energy, and a feeling of youthful vitality—come with the package. They are the reward and the greatest single return on investment imaginable.

This is not something you can buy. You can't delegate it. You have to do the work yourself. But the key is to make that work fun, to make your workouts enjoyable. Instead of, "No pain, no gain," my mantra is, "The best workout is the one you like enough to keep doing it."

This is a book for those of you who enjoy lifting weights or who are interested in what it's all about. As you will see, I believe in using photographs of yourself as great motivators for sticking with it. For instance, here is a good example of the front lat spread pose that shows photos of me at three different stages of life—as a teenager, an adult, and a senior—with the theme being **a lifetime of lifting weights.**

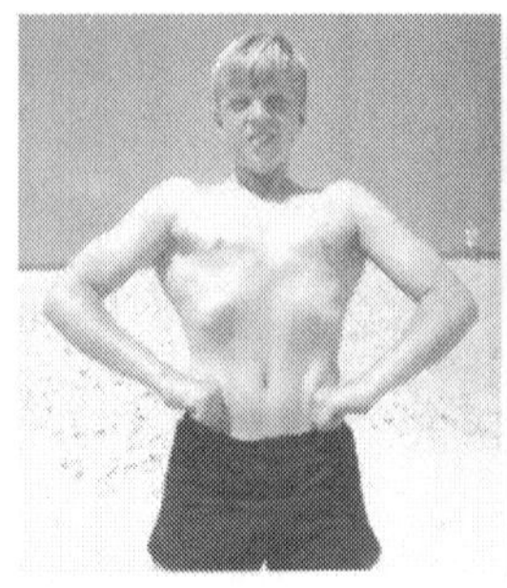

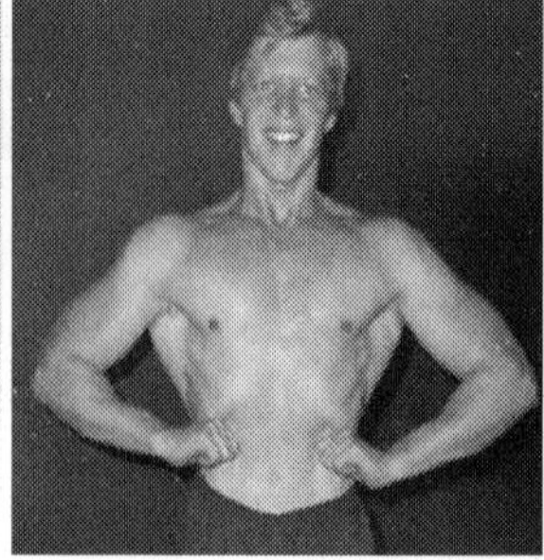

**Age fourteen** **Age thirty-two** **Age sixty**

Displaying photos of what I have achieved is a visual reinforcement that motivates me to continue training. Too many bodybuilders reach their goals and then stop exercising altogether. That defeats the whole purpose, which, though it begins with vanity, should end with health and fitness. That is what helps us feel youthful and energetic in our golden years.

It is no wonder that many distinguished historical figures were interested in bodybuilding, ranging from the Sherlock Holmes creator, Sir Arthur Conan Doyle, to the person known for decades as "the richest man in the world," J. Paul Getty, to one of the most celebrated actors in Hollywood, Sean Connery. So, if you are interested in bodybuilding, know that you are in good company.

I hope you enjoy my story. I found it cathartic to write, and I hope you find it motivating to read. Incidentally, I was sixty-eight when the cover photo of this book was taken.

CHAPTER ONE

~ ~ ~ ~ ~

# AN INSPIRED START

There is something magical about lifting weights. I've been doing it my whole life, and it has shaped my destiny, from childhood to my "golden years." It has helped me feel youthful my entire life. This is my story, and I hope it inspires you to find the fountain of youth that, for me, is as close as wrapping my fingers around a barbell or dumbbell.

My journey started more than a half-century ago, when I saw this picture:

I was twelve years old and riding my bicycle near our home in suburban Chicago. In those days, it was safe for kids to ride their bikes all over town on their own.

I stopped at the Linden Street L station in Wilmette, where they had a newsstand with dozens of magazines and newspapers. I always wanted to see the latest sports magazine, or maybe something about wrestling or boxing, with covers showing men who looked like gladiators with bloody faces from their battles.

As I glanced at the colorful magazine covers, I saw that *Strength & Health* and stopped in my tracks. "What is that?? *Who* is that??" It was the most incredible sight I had ever seen. I felt like I had been knocked out.

I had never seen *Strength & Health* or any other muscle magazine. The man on the cover was standing in front of what looked like the Roman ruins, and he looked like a real-life Superman.

When I was seven, I had tried jumping off our front porch to fly, just like I had seen Superman do on television. But instead of flying, I simply jumped from the porch to the ground. I knew I couldn't fly.

When I saw that muscleman, holding one arm in the air with a clenched fist and making a bicep pose with the other arm, I thought, I can do that. I dug into my pocket and paid the thirty-five cents that the magazine cost. It was dated March 1963. I was born on August 8, 1950, so I was twelve when I bought that magazine and started bodybuilding.

I pedaled home as fast as I could and went up to my room. For most of my childhood, I had shared a bedroom with my older brother Ray, but my parents bought a bigger house in 1959 and had the attic converted into three bedrooms for Ray, Rob, and me, plus whatever cousins or relatives were staying with us. I was one of eight kids, so we had at least ten people in the same house, counting my mom and dad, at all times.

**This family photo was taken shortly after I bought my first muscle magazine. I was just a kid (I am the boy farthest to the left in the back row).**

I started reading that magazine—and reading and reading—and I really couldn't stop. That same night, my parents took us out to a smorgasbord dinner in Evanston, and I brought the magazine with me. I couldn't bear to part with it.

That was one of the advantages of being one of eight kids. There was always so much noise and confusion that my parents didn't notice I hardly paid any attention to dinner, except for reading about how important good nutrition was for bodybuilding. I looked at the musclemen on the back cover and vowed that someday I would have arms as thick as theirs, not to mention giant shoulder, chest, and back muscles.

I went back to the newsstand the following week and bought Joe Weider's *Muscle Builder and Power* and *Mr. America* magazines, and I was hooked. Only later, when visiting downtown Chicago, did I discover Peary Rader's *Iron Man* magazine. And then, a year after that, Bob Hoffman and John Grimek, both of whom were responsible for *Strength & Health*, founded *Muscular Development* magazine. I read them all, cover to cover—every article, every photo caption, every ad, even the classifieds in tiny type.

My mother said she had Joe Weider and Bob Hoffman to thank for me becoming such a voracious reader later in life. I told that story to Joe Weider over lunch a few years before he died at age ninety-three, and he said Arnold Schwarzenegger's mom said something similar. "She said, 'We have Joe Weider to thank for Arnold learning English,'" Joe explained. Arnold's mother told Joe, "He'd get those muscle magazines in English and run to his Austrian friends who were fluent in English and shout, 'What does it say?? What does it say??'"

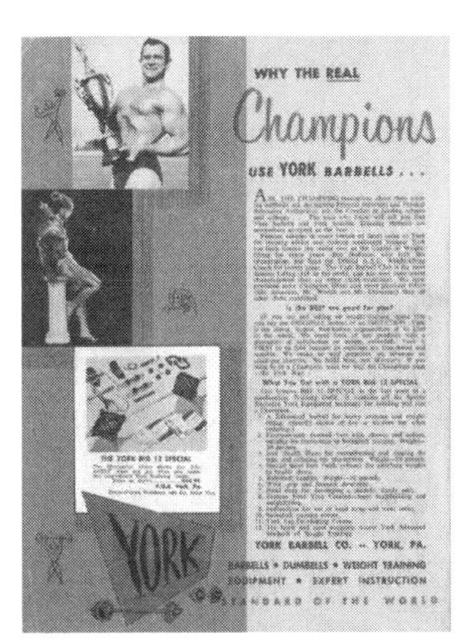


Unlike Arnold, who wanted to conquer the world of bodybuilding, movies, and politics, my goal was more modest. It was to have more muscles than the man in the blue bathing suit on that first cover that I had seen on *Strength & Health*

magazine. That was my goal, and I vowed that nothing would stop me from reaching it.

Did I reach it? Yes, I did.

But it took twenty-three years, and that included twelve years in which I had given up entirely. Twelve years in which I persuaded myself that this wasn't really important, that this was kid's stuff, that I was interested in intellectual pursuits, which was true, and thus had no time for muscle building, which was false.

In this book, I will tell you what happened, and I hope it inspires you to lift weights—either as a beginner who is just getting started or as an old pro who wants to continue working out harder than ever.

**Ages thirteen and thirty-two. Persistence…**

By the time I reached my goal, at age thirty-five, I had become a bodybuilder for life. Not a competitive, award-winning bodybuilder, but someone whose life was shaped and enhanced by pumping iron as a hobby. I love to work out, though for a number of years, I refused to acknowledge that.

My story took a lot of twists and turns, and unnecessary suffering, as I pretended I had outgrown my childhood dream. I begin telling you about my journey by trying to remember what my feelings were like nearly sixty years ago, when I vowed that someday, I would have as much muscle as the man on the cover.

By the time I reached that goal, I had a full life with business, family, church, travel, and hobbies, and I was pleasantly surprised to discover that there were many rewards beyond muscles that came from lifting weights. But pumping iron made everything else possible, and it still does as I am writing this in my seventies.

Feeling young and energetic is something that I have taken for granted since my thirties, and now, as I look back on the intervening years, I realize that lifting weights was the key. It is magical.

**Age thirty-five**

I start by telling you stories about becoming a bodybuilder at heart as a little kid, meeting people who were world-famous in the sport, and vowing never to give up. But I did give up, at least for a while, and I try to understand what happened and how I allowed my dream to slip away—and then how it reemerged, deep from within, and I said, I will do this, no matter what.

Then I explain how everything came together for me at just the right time and how certain individuals, especially Arnold Schwarzenegger and Franco Columbu, helped make my success possible, not because of their bodies but because of their minds—because of their relentlessly positive attitudes and encouragement.

Once I achieved my goal, it never occurred to me to stop working out. I had become a bodybuilder for life, and I try to give examples of how I have continued to reinforce that image for so many decades, one workout at a time, and how I stayed motivated to keep training—for a lifetime. There is a famous Chinese proverb: "A journey of a thousand miles begins with a single step." So, let me walk you through my journey, one step at a time.

CHAPTER TWO

~ ~ ~ ~ ~

# DREAMING OF MUSCLES

What I learned, as I look back on it more than a half-century later, was the importance of persistence, of hanging in there and never giving up, no matter what. At the same time, I learned about something called "muscle memory," which, for bodybuilders, means that if you put on muscle and then lose it later, you will find it very easy to regain once you start lifting weights again. In a big picture sense, it means that every effort you exert in pursuit of your goals will pay off, even if you feel like a total failure at the time.

But long before I felt like a total failure, I was excited and enthusiastic about building a championship body. As I was reading those magazines, I would try to do the exercises in the photos. I went to sleep at night dreaming of building my muscles. I put up pictures from the magazines all over my room and down in the basement, where I kept my weights and a York bench my parents bought for me.

There was a photo in one of the magazines showing a young bodybuilder named Rock Stonewall, and the magazine said he worked at Eaton's Health Food Store on Van Buren Street in downtown

Chicago. I called the store and asked to speak to Rock and was blown away when he said, "Hello." I couldn't believe it. I was talking to a champion bodybuilder! I asked if it would be okay if I visited him in person, and he said of course.

So, we hung up, and I rushed into the living room to ask my parents if they knew where Van Buren Street was and if I could see him. They said yes, and a week later, on a Friday afternoon, my mom and I drove downtown, first to pick up my dad from work and then to visit this Mr. America contender.

Rock was in his midtwenties at the time, but because I was twelve, I had no conception of age. To me, he was an adult, while I was still a child. He had a charismatic smile and incredible muscles and could not have been more friendly. He sold us some vitamins and asked if we had visited the gym next door. What gym?

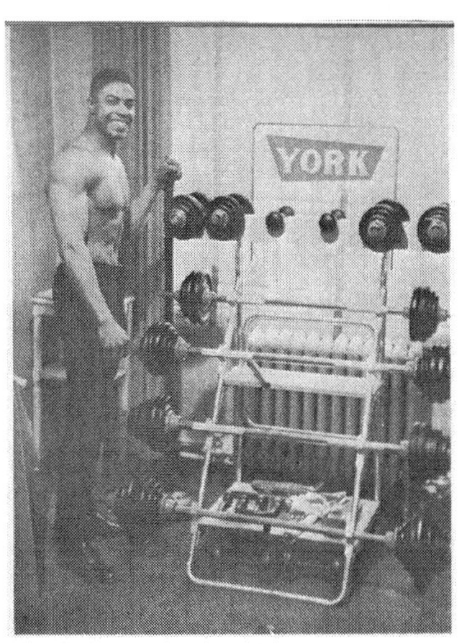


**Rock Stonewall**

"It's called Triumph Gym," he said. "You just walk to the brown brick building on your right as you leave the store and take the elevator to the third floor." We did, and the three of us barely fit into that old elevator. It was the kind that had a steel cage that you close manually before the elevator would start. It seemed to take ten minutes to get up three floors, but the wait was worth it.

I saw more than a dozen men lifting weights, a handful of whom were serious bodybuilders, and I was just so excited to be there. I wanted to work out on the spot. Remember, I was only twelve.

The manager was named Bill Jacobs, and he had big, muscular arms with a tight-fitting, short-sleeved white dress shirt. Bill was very friendly.

My dad explained that I was interested in lifting weights, and we had just met Rock Stonewall, who recommended we visit the gym. They talked for a while, while I gawked at the sight of all those guys having such a great time working out. *I could not imagine a more fun way to spend a Friday night.* That is how enthusiastic I was about bodybuilding.

I started working out in my basement gym and persuaded many of my friends to join in. Ed Hoban's dad made squat racks and benches for a gym that Ed and his brother Hank worked out in at their house. Pretty soon, a half-dozen of my classmates were reading the muscle magazines, and we would all work out together at various times, either at my gym or at the Hoban's.

It is interesting that twenty-five years later, Ed Hoban was living in Aspen and was friends with the brilliant writer Hunter Thompson. Talk about small worlds—because I was syndicating Hunter's newspaper column, but Ed and I did not discover that we had this mutual connection until after Hunter's death.

One of my favorite training partners was Luke Matthews, who became best friends in high school with the famous actor Bill Murray. They went to Regis College in Denver together, where they were roommates.

In 2014, we had a fiftieth reunion at "Faith Hope" (the nickname for our school). Most of the people in my class had spent kindergarten through eighth grade together. In other words, at the age when our minds were like wet cement, during some of our most formative years, we spent all day together, and then most of us went our separate ways for fifty years.

At the reunion, one of my classmates, Stephen Dowdle, who was a successful businessman, asked me how I knew there would be a fitness revolution in later years. "How were you so ahead of your time?" he asked. I felt complimented by his question, but I knew that this was pure luck on my part. I told the truth and said that I didn't have a clue about the future. I just knew I wanted to build big muscles.

We would buy Hoffman's soy protein powder and mix it with milk and drink it by the gallon. They called it Hi-Proteen, with the word "protein" deliberately misspelled. I suspect they spelled it that way because so many of their customers were in their teens. We would eat Hoffman's protein fudge bars before and after doing hundreds of sit-ups and leg raises. I went to sleep every night reading muscle magazines, dreaming of the day when my physique would look like the man on that cover.

When I was thirteen, I started taking the L to downtown Chicago—alone, which is unfathomable today—to see my friend Rock Stonewall. In between taking care of customers, he would write out workout programs for me and answer my endless stream of questions. He was always patient and cheerful.

Every hour, he went to the back room to do one-legged calf raises, twenty-four reps for each leg, eight with his foot pointed out, eight with his foot pointed straight, and eight with his foot pointed in. A carpenter had made a little wooden step, with a sponge on top to serve as a cushion for his feet. He took off his shoes but kept his socks on. I copied his movements, using the stairs at home, and what a pump my calves got! I loved the soreness I would feel in my calves for the next day or two.

When you lift weights a lot, you learn that there is a good sore and a bad sore. A good sore occurs when a muscle has been exercised and challenged, and the recovery includes a warm kind of soreness the next day that goes away in a short period of time. A bad sore occurs when you tear a ligament or strain a joint—something that you intuitively know is serious—and recovery can take months. The longer you train, the more you learn about your body, and the easier it is to avoid injury.

One Saturday, my father rode downtown with me, and we visited Triumph Gym again. He wanted to chat with Bill Jacobs, who gave me permission to work out. I was probably thirteen at the time, but I was small for my age—barely five feet tall and ninety pounds—which, no doubt, had much to do with my wanting to get big.

Vince Gironda, a muscle man whose Los Angeles gym featured star bodybuilders and Hollywood celebrities during the 1960s and '70s, wrote that the easy gainers, the guys who played football and naturally had a lot of muscle, rarely stuck with a weight training program for a long period of time. It was the hard gainers, he said, the guys who really had to struggle to make progress, who stuck with it and succeeded in the long run.

I remember in the 1980s working out outside at World Gym in Santa Monica next to Dr. Sam Wilson, a brilliant psychiatrist and an avid weightlifter, and I asked him if he had a theory about why some people are determined to develop a massive amount of muscle. He said, "I think it always starts from a feeling of smallness, where they want to make themselves bigger."

**Vince Gironda**

Well, that was me at age thirteen. As I did bench presses and squats, following the routines Rock had written down for me, my dad was chatting with Bill Jacobs. It turned out that Bill's father had had a car dealership on the North Shore, and Bill had grown up in Wilmette. He started his life wanting to be a professional baseball player, which he did in Mexico for a while, but an injury put an end to his dreams. So, he took up bodybuilding.

My dad wanted to know if it was safe for me to work out alone at the gym, which looked like it could have been a converted apartment—which gives you an idea of how small it was. But with wall-to-wall mirrors, it looked enormous to my thirteen-year-old eyes.

As I look back on it, I picture a little boy who was dreaming of building big muscles alongside he-men from all over the city of Chicago. I was not cautious or even slightly apprehensive. I wanted to dive in where the water was deep, and I was sure to emerge victorious. That is how I felt, not knowing that there was a secret enemy waiting to attack me.

CHAPTER THREE

~ ~ ~ ~ ~

# ATTENDING MY FIRST BODYBUILDING CONTEST

That secret enemy was cynicism and self-doubt. They are killers. They are the difference between reaching your dreams in life or withdrawing into failure. That is the most important lesson I have learned in seventy years of living.

But when I had only thirteen years of living and knew nothing about this, I was just excited to be able to work out at a real bodybuilding gym. I later learned that Triumph Gym had been founded by a man named Irvin Johnson.

I actually met him in 1982, when he was known as Rheo Blair and selling some of the best bodybuilding supplements on the market. He provided supplements and nutritional advice to tennis legend Bobby Riggs and other celebrities. I saw a movie on an airplane recently about the 1973 tennis "Battle of the Sexes" between Billie Jean King and Bobby Riggs, and the character of Rheo Blair was featured prominently.

Bill Jacobs told my father yes, the gym would be safe for me because he was always there, and if there were any problems, he would get involved. Wow, was I happy! So, every Saturday, I would take the L to downtown Chicago, walk over to chat with Rock, and then go upstairs for my workout.

When I graduated from eighth grade, my parents gave me a summer membership at Triumph Gym, and I was happier than I can ever remember! This was the summer of 1964. In the fall, I was going to start at Quigley Seminary in downtown Chicago to study to become a Catholic priest. I didn't really want to be a priest, but Quigley was the only school in downtown Chicago that my mom, a devout Italian Catholic, would let me go to.

That didn't work out so well, because Quigley made us do sports in the afternoon, and I was on the swimming team and had virtually no time to see Rock or to work out at Triumph Gym, so after my first year of high school, I switched to Loyola Academy in Wilmette.

But during that summer, between eighth grade and high school, I had a ball. There was another kid my age named Rocky, who trained at Triumph Gym, too, and we became lifting partners. Rocky was skinny but strong for his size. We both felt so cool, so grown up, working out for a couple of hours and then taking a shower, getting dressed, and going to eat at Tad's $1.19 Steakhouse at the busy corner of Van Buren Street and Wabash Avenue, with the L thundering overhead.

Rocky would always complain that his steak tasted like "shoe leather," and that made me feel grown up, too. I didn't know you were allowed to complain about the food in a restaurant. That's how my parents had brought us up, to always be polite and grateful.

To me, the food was delicious. It was cafeteria-style: We got a baked potato, green salad, and garlic bread with the steak, and I devoured it all. I felt big and pumped up from working out.

That feeling after a hard weight training workout, where your muscles are pumped up with blood, is like no other. Top it off with a big meal, rest, and relaxation, and life just doesn't get any better.

This is what Arnold Schwarzenegger meant when he was interviewed for the documentary film *Pumping Iron* and compared the pump from lifting weights to having an orgasm.

Attending my first bodybuilding contest was a real thrill. It was held on the north side of Chicago somewhere—I think it was the Irving Park YMCA or the Duncan Y or something similar—and I went there with some of my classmates.

In those days, they had Olympic weightlifting events for hours and hours, and you couldn't believe how tedious that became for us kids who just wanted to see the musclemen. When they finally held the bodybuilding contest, there was maybe one lightbulb overhead in a completely dark room. Compared with bodybuilding contests today, it was barbaric.

But at the same time, there was something much more authentic, genuine, and positive about these shows because there were very few drugs involved, and the enthusiasm of the audience was so personal and heartfelt. After all, most of the people clapping knew the contestants. They were mostly guys who trained hard, drank protein shakes, and did a handful of poses they had seen in the magazine pictures.

It was easy to go backstage, because security was nonexistent. The contest was for Mr. Chicagoland, and backstage, the contestants were pumping up with dumbbells, push-ups, and stretches.

We saw two giants—guys with as much muscle as Rock Stonewall—and I couldn't believe it. They were guest posers. One was Bill Seno, a powerlifter and bodybuilder. He was in his midtwenties and could lift huge poundages. His goal was to get his bench press from 450 pounds to 500! He had an incredibly solid build, and he patiently took the time to answer all of our questions.

I remember that he had a tick in his eyes, where he kept blinking as if he were nervous. Maybe it was just a temporary thing, or maybe he had sweat in his eyes, but after meeting him, I started blinking my eyes the same way. I couldn't bench press 500 pounds, but I could blink my eyes. Everyone was worried that something was wrong with me because I was blinking all the time, but after my mom said we should see a doctor, I decided to stop.

**Bill Seno**

Pumping up next to Bill Seno was a monster, someone with muscles like I had never seen before—bigger than anyone in the magazines. His name was Sergio Oliva, and he had recently defected from Cuba. He spoke very little English, but he was friendly and kind. That night was his first appearance as a bodybuilder in America.

Through a translator, Sergio told us that he had been an Olympic weightlifter in Cuba and had defected and recently arrived in America. He worked as a television technician. He later became a well-known and respected Chicago policeman. This was his first posing exhibition as a bodybuilder in America, and he was nervous. His muscles were off-the-charts incredible, so it was no surprise that he would go on to become one of the greatest bodybuilders of all time. As a kid, I had no way of knowing the historical significance of seeing Sergio Oliva posing in America for the first time.

**Sergio Oliva (left) in 1964, just starting his legendary bodybuilding career.**

**Sergio Oliva (right) as "The Myth" in later years.**

Sergio's nickname was "The Myth" because no one could believe that a human being could have so much muscle. He was the king of bodybuilding for many years, until a young Arnold Schwarzenegger dethroned him.

Sitting in the back seat of my friend's father's car on the way home after seeing all those muscles, I vowed to train harder than ever. When I went to Triumph Gym during the summer of 1964, I frequently stopped in at a Catholic church on the way to the train station. I would sit in the back of the church and ask Jesus to help me stick with it until I had as much muscle as the fellow on the magazine cover. I felt like a child who wanted to become a man, yes, but not just any man. I had a specific goal for how I wanted to look.

As I look back now, trying to understand why I quit at fifteen before starting again in my late twenties, I can see that I allowed criticism and negative voices to beat me down. I did not know how to set short-term goals or how to appreciate the gains I was making.

I remember when some of my friends came over to our house on a summer day, and we were in the basement gym. They had been driven there by a kid who was going to start college in the fall. He was very loud and a little strange, being an eighteen-year-old who was hanging out with fourteen-year-olds, and he saw the pictures of bodybuilders on my wall and started mocking them. He mimicked the poses and said what losers they were. Today, I would have sent him packing. But at the time, being fourteen, I absorbed what he said and laughed along with my friends.

Also, I was late in going through puberty, and many of my friends put on more muscle because of the increase in their testosterone, which came later for me. That was very discouraging at the time.

There were other factors as well, such as having no control over my schedule and the distractions of being a teenager in 1964, when the world was changing pretty dramatically. In the end, those negative voices won, and I lost, and I am telling my story now to give you hope and inspiration.

If you are a baby boomer and haven't worked out in years, you could gain enormous benefits from lifting weights. And they don't have to be gigantic poundages either. Even light dumbbells will improve your circulation, help you sleep better, and, over time, increase your bone density.

I never had that in mind when I was thirteen or thirty; it is something I discovered when I turned forty and then fifty and then sixty and now seventy. I really do look forward to each new decade, always excited about new adventures that I am able to enjoy because I feel so full of life as a result of this amazing discovery.

CHAPTER FOUR

~ ~ ~ ~ ~

# MR. AMERICA 1964 AND 1968

During that summer of 1964, the Mr. America contest was held at Lane Tech High School in Chicago. The sponsoring organization was the Amateur Athletic Union, or the AAU, and one of the local organizers was a man named Joseph Paul. He had been a weightlifter in his youth and now was a French teacher in his sixties. He taught at New Trier High School, which was in my hometown of Winnetka.

Mr. Paul, as I called him, told me about visiting France and eating six-course meals and enjoying the food so much. He was a wiry guy—all muscle and no fat—but he was not used to pressure or business management. While getting ready for the Mr. America contest, he said he lost twenty pounds from worry, and he looked it. He used to tell me that at my age, I should do no more than three sets per body part three times a week. Any more training than that would be overtraining and lead to a loss of muscle.

I really didn't want to hear that. I wanted to train two or three hours a day, six days a week, just like the champs in Joe Weider's magazines. Looking back fifty years later, I think we were both right. He was right that I was overtraining, and I was right that his program did not appeal to me, and I probably would not have stuck with it.

The most important thing I have learned during a lifetime of lifting weights is that you have to find workout programs you really enjoy.

**John Grimek**

Still, I was making progress. I remember calling *Strength & Health* magazine and asking to speak to John Grimek. He had been an Olympic lifting champion and Mr. America and Mr. Universe. In fact, he kept winning contests so easily that the organizers had to make special rules to prevent him from competing because it started to become boring watching the same guy win year after year. What I love about Grimek's physique is that, during his prime, there were no steroids involved. He had about as good a build as you can get naturally.

I don't remember what we talked about. I think I was so excited that my call went through that I just blubbered something about how excited I was to be on the phone with him. I wrote up my story and sent in a photo, and they ran it in the November 1964 issue of *Muscular Development* magazine!

**BOY GOES FROM 86 TO 102 POUNDS**

A sixteen pound gain was registered by young Rich Newcombe of Winnetka, Ill. during 30 days of this summer.

Rich used a good routine of Bench Presses (5 sets), Presses (four sets), Curls, Rowing and Squats (three sets each) along with 25 repetition Situps during each training session.

He ate a lot of fruit, especially dried raisins, apricots and prunes. Two quarts of milk every day along with meats, eggs and cheese. He stopped eating candy, cakes and pies and substituted Hoffman's Carab Tablets and Coconut Proteen Powder.

Rich's before and after measurements are:—

| | BEFORE | 30 DAYS LATER | GAINS |
|---|---|---|---|
| Weight | 86 | 102 | 16 |
| Chest | 30 | 34 | 4 |
| Arms | 11 | 11¾ | ¾ |
| Thighs | 18 | 20 | 2 |
| Calves | 12½ | 13 | ½ |

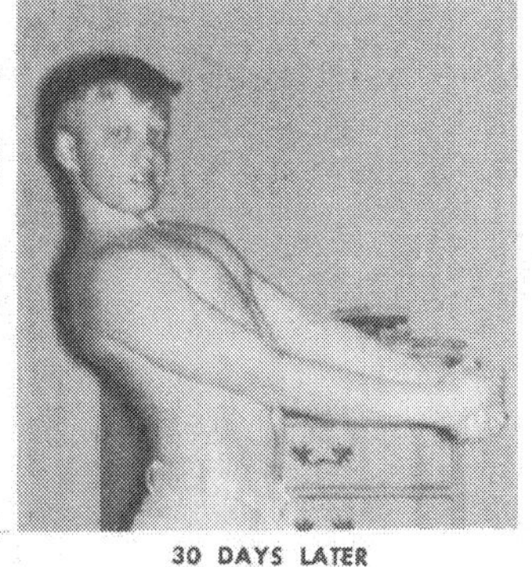

30 DAYS LATER

I remember getting a ride from one of my friend's parents to the Mr. America contest. They dropped me off, and as I was walking on the pavement of the high school hosting the contest, I spotted John Grimek standing outside next to a tall, husky man. Grimek's arms and chest gave him away. They were enormous! As I got closer, I realized the tall man was Bob Hoffman, who was leaning against a circular high-top table eating lunch. He looked like he hadn't eaten in days, which, given his hectic schedule, might have been true.

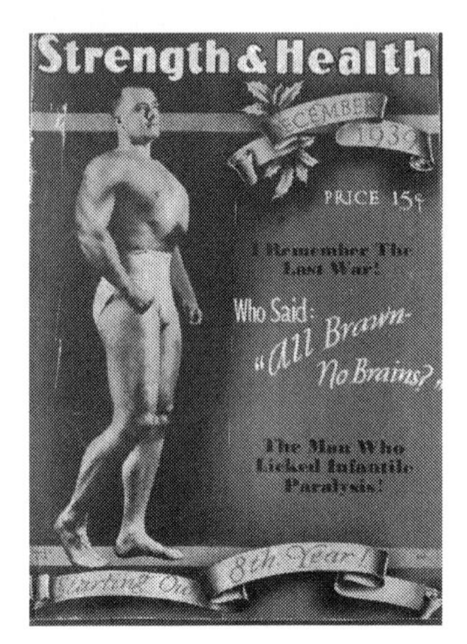


**Bob Hoffman**

Not being bashful, I immediately said hello, shook hands, and told them what an honor it was to meet them. Grimek smiled and said, "Good to meet you. Thank you for coming. We always need new blood in the sport." Hoffman, who, understandably, did not want to be bothered while eating, said hello, but he reminded me of the fellow at the circus who says, "Go away, kid; you're bothering me."

Inside, I watched the posing and was as inspired as ever. This was during the day, what is called "prejudging," when the judges actually rate each competitor and decide who the winners are. But they don't announce that until the evening, when the auditorium is filled and there is better lighting, more dramatic posing, and what looks like a real contest. Not having a car, I could only attend the prejudging and had to be home that night. No matter. I just loved watching all those guys who were determined enough to stick with it.

**Val Vasilef (left), Bill Seno (center), and Sergio Oliva accepting their awards for "Most Muscular."**

In my opinion, the winners were Sergio Oliva first and Bill Seno second. But that's not the way it turned out. A fellow named Val Vasilef won—and he turned out to be a great champion. In fact, he has written his life story in a book called *Russian Bear,* and he pays tribute to John Grimek in a YouTube video, which I really respect.

My preference for Bill and Sergio was partly related to the fact that they were the only two men on stage I had met, but it was also because they were the most massively muscled. In fact, Bill Seno was awarded the "Most Muscular" prize, which I never understood. I thought the whole point of a Mr. America contest was to see who had the most muscles. Since Seno did, according to the judges, why was he not Mr. America?

As for Sergio Oliva, the judges, including my friend Joe Paul, ranked him seventh! That was totally insane but not unusual for AAU bodybuilding contests in those days. The AAU was primarily involved with Olympic weightlifting. Bob Hoffman's first love was always Olympic weightlifting, and he coached the American team for years. To the AAU, bodybuilding was a spinoff, which was why they always had those day-long weightlifting contests before they would allow a bodybuilding show later at night for an hour or so.

In competition with the AAU was the growing International Federation of Body Builders, or IFBB. This was the brainchild of Ben Weider, whose brother, Joe, was publishing competing magazines to Bob Hoffman's, and who was selling exercise equipment and nutritional supplements, just like the York Barbell company. Their rivalry was intense, and nearly everyone was forced—by Hoffman—to choose sides.

My friend Rock Stonewall was in the IFBB, and once you competed there, you were banned from competing in the AAU events. Knowing what I know now, I don't blame Rock a bit. He knew that at that time, the AAU would not give Black bodybuilders a fair shake. Sergio found out firsthand, and only a year later, he joined the IFBB and won the Mr. America, Mr. Universe, and Mr. Olympia contests within a few years, which he justly deserved.

These were the early 1960s, a few years after the start of peaceful civil rights protests and a few years before the rioting that came in the late '60s. My father was anti-prejudice. He felt really strongly about not seeing color or race. He grew up on a farm in Minnesota, and I am not sure why he was so passionately against racism, but he always was.

He would get angry when he heard racist comments, and there were plenty in those days. It's funny, but we never discussed Rock Stonewall's race. I was twelve when I first met him, and he could have been black, white, or green, and I wouldn't have noticed. All I could see were MUSCLES. I knew I wanted to build my muscles like Rock. Some of my friends asked me if my parents were concerned that Rock was Black, and I remember saying that was ridiculous. Of course not.

**Rock Stonewall (left) with one of his friends. Rock worked out at a home gym on the South Side of Chicago.**

At the same time, Rock was in fantastic shape for the 1968 Mr. America contest, and he lost to Frank Zane, who, a month later, beat Arnold Schwarzenegger in the Mr. Universe contest. Rock attributed his loss to racism, but I am not convinced. He said he won the prejudging and assumed he was finally going to be crowned Mr. America. His brother-in-law was Leroy Colbert, who had been in the Weider inner circle and was frequently featured in Weider magazines.

Leroy told him before the winner was announced, "I smell a rat." Rock was devastated when he discovered that Frank Zane had beaten him. "That was crazy," he said later. "I should have won. The only reason I lost was because of racism."

Now, it is true that Rock was great in 1968, in peak shape with a fantastic posing routine, but Frank Zane had all that and probably more. I say that because Frank went on to beat Arnold in the Mr. Universe contest a few weeks later, and a few years after that, he was crowned Mr. Olympia three years in a row—in 1977, '78, and '79.

What I am saying is that while I personally did not see Rock as a Black man, he saw himself as one and felt that the judges would never treat him equally with whites in a competition. He felt victimized and started leading a much different life. He tried to make a comeback in 1975 and looked good, but he wound up being just another competitor, while Frank Zane went on to become a legend in bodybuilding.

**Rock Stonewall (left) in peak condition in 1968. Frank Zane (right) in 1968, a few weeks after beating everyone, including Rock Stonewall, in the Mr. America contest and then beating everyone, including Arnold Schwarzenegger (at far right), in the Mr. Universe contest.**

CHAPTER FIVE

~ ~ ~ ~ ~

# PROFESSIONAL PHOTOGRAPHS

I ran into Rock in 1982, and I'll get to that in a minute, but I want to stay in 1964 a little longer. During that summer when I would meet Rocky at Triumph Gym every day, work out for a couple of hours, and eat lunch at the $1.19 steakhouse, we were both making good progress, but we didn't know it. One day, Rock told me he was posing for a photographer that night and asked if Rocky and I wanted to come along and have our pictures taken.

**Rock Stonewall**

OMG, how exciting! I had posing trunks in my gym bag—why, I have no idea—and Rocky had some in his apartment in Logan Square. I called my mom and asked permission, and she said fine. As I said, that was one of the many advantages of being one of eight children: I got permission to do things a lot faster than many of my friends. I'm sure she was busy with some of my younger brothers and sisters and just wanted to get off the phone.

Rocky asked me if I would take the L to his apartment with him so his mom could meet me and see that this was all on the up and up. We did, and Rocky got his trunks. We took the L back to see Rock at Eaton's Health Food Store. Someone picked us up in a car and drove a few miles to a tattoo parlor on the South Side.

We walked inside the tattoo parlor and saw some rough-looking people, and I just smiled and said "hi." They said "hi" back and ignored me and Rocky. We were with Rock. It never occurred to me that these guys had the same name until just now! And this was twelve years before Sylvester Stallone made the name "Rocky" world-famous as a boxer in the movies, following legends in the ring such as Rocky Marciano and Rocky Graziano.

Rock had obviously been here before, because he knew where to go—a room in the back that had a big screen against a wall and photographic lights. Rock took off his clothes and put on his posing briefs. He had baby oil and started rubbing a light coating all over his body. He asked if we would put it on his back, so we did.

A week later, we got our pictures…and I was devastated. I didn't look anything like the men in the magazines. I had been lifting weights and eating tons of protein for two years, and I could not see any progress.

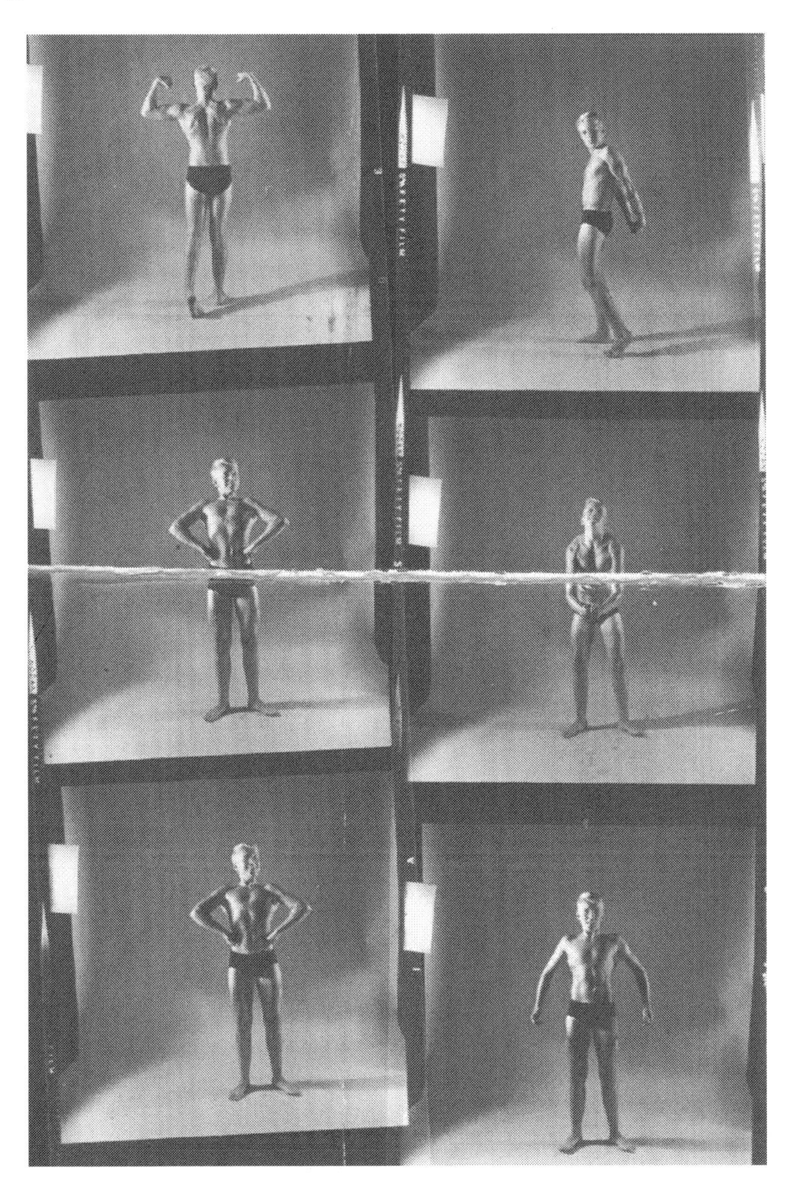

I was hypercritical of myself, and that contributed in a major way to my short-term failure. Instead of seeing the progress that I was making, all I could see were flaws in my physique. Of course, compared with Mr. America, I looked like a little kid. But at thirteen, when those photos were taken, I *was* a little kid. What I did not see were the major gains I had been making.

Despite my feelings of inadequacy, I continued lifting weights throughout my freshman year of high school, but I was on the swimming team and had practice many afternoons.

The summer between my freshman and sophomore year, my mom took all eight kids to the south of France, to a small seaside village called Cap Ferret. It was an island of sand between the Atlantic Ocean and Arcachon Bay. We went swimming every day, and I did a lot of freehand exercises—push-ups, chin-ups, sit-ups—but there were no weights.

**Bill Pearl**

I remember looking at a picture of Bill Pearl, with his massive lats, chest, and arms, and just willing myself to look the same—but I lacked the control to do anything about it. I wasn't old enough to drive a car, and there was no gym around. I do remember once going to a gym in Bordeaux. I don't remember how we got there, but I'll never forget the ride home. The man driving was a maniac. I don't think cars had seat belts in those days, and I vividly remember his speedometer hitting 160. That was in kilometers, but still, that's close to 100 miles per hour.

My mom had taken all eight of us, and we lived in a little rented house called Villa Chouanette, which had two or three rooms for ten people—the eight kids, my mom, and a seventeen-year-old French girl hired to help out named Nicolle Foussatt. Nicolle was kind, and we met her family in Bordeaux. I think that is how I was able to go to that gym. We must have gone to Bordeaux to visit Nicolle's family, and she had a friend who drove me after my workout back to Cap Ferret because he was staying there that weekend.

My father flew over at the end of July, and we spent the month of August sightseeing in France and Italy. I remember walking on the boardwalk in Nice one night and seeing this heavily muscled Black man wearing a white polo shirt and white pants, walking along and doing a sort of "bodybuilder strut," where he spread out his lats and kept his giant arms at his side. He had perfected that walk, and he had a naturally slim waist, which accentuated his lat spread. I noticed that people would stare at him as he passed them.

Ray and I followed him from maybe twenty feet behind. I wanted to run up and introduce myself and try to communicate with him in my limited but quickly improving French and sign language, but there were too many people around to do that comfortably.

After we got home and I saw some new muscle magazines, I realized his name was Serge Nubret, and he became a world-famous bodybuilder who competed against Arnold Schwarzenegger in the Mr. Olympia contest featured in the documentary *Pumping Iron.*

**Serge Nubret**

After arriving home, having turned fifteen that August and being in a band, I decided to switch from Quigley to Loyola. In other words, rather than living as an outsider among my friends—obsessed with bodybuilding and going to school downtown every day—I abandoned my dream of looking like Guy Mierczuk on that magazine cover and started living the life I was supposed to live, in conformity with the people I had grown up with.

This was a really difficult period in my life, and I started acting as if I had never lifted a weight. I just felt so discouraged. I only stayed at Loyola for one semester and then transferred to New Trier, our local public high school. My grades were awful. We went on a family vacation to Washington, D.C., and I fell in love with the campus of Georgetown University, but there was no way I could get in.

My father told me about a new college preparatory school in Indiana called La Lumiere. The headmaster said I had a shot at getting into Georgetown if I repeated my junior year and really got serious about studying. While there, away from distractions, I fell in love with reading and writing. My intellectual curiosity became insatiable. I was in the school's second graduating class, with only sixteen students. La Lumiere is still small, and its alumni are very accomplished, including Supreme Court Chief Justice John Roberts and the actor and comedian Jim Gaffigan. I donated my old York bench and barbells to the school.

I did get into Georgetown, where I met and fell in love with Carole in 1969 (we were married in 1975). I sailed through college in three years and graduated Phi Beta Kappa and magna cum laude, and I also was one of the founding editors of *The Georgetown Voice*, an alternative newspaper that celebrated its fiftieth anniversary in 2019.

**Larry Scott**

During that time, I only occasionally thought about my old bodybuilding days. I do remember buying some of Larry Scott's courses by mail and signing up at a gym in Northern Virginia, and it was amazing how much progress I made in just a few months, but for the most part, I felt that I had "outgrown" that phase of my life. Little did I know how wrong I was.

CHAPTER SIX

~ ~ ~ ~ ~

# MEETING ARNOLD

During the next five years, as I was getting my business and journalism career off the ground, I smoked cigarettes and almost never made it to the gym. In 1977, when I was living in Baltimore, I joined a Holiday Health Club. I also started buying vitamins from Rheo Blair in Hollywood.

But again, these workouts were nowhere near as important to me as they had been. I was the twenty-six-year-old Baltimore bureau chief for United Press International, smoking close to two packs a day, drinking tons of coffee all day, and, at least a couple of nights a week, drinking shots of whiskey followed by pints of beer. I remember getting a physical exam, and the doctor told me that if I didn't change, I was likely to start gaining weight, maybe five pounds a year for the next ten or fifteen years, and that alarmed me.

While working as a reporter and editor in the UPI newsroom in Baltimore, we received dozens of press releases every day, and one of my jobs was to sift through them to look for something newsworthy. I remember reading about a man named Arnold Schwarzenegger, who was a bodybuilding star. He was promoting his book about his bodybuilding career.

I ordered a "review copy," which meant I got it for free because I might write a review of the book, which would help boost its sales. I really enjoyed reading it. His stories brought me back to my early bodybuilding days. I called Simon & Schuster and said that if Arnold ever came through Baltimore, I wanted to write a story about him for UPI. They got back to me pretty quickly, and we arranged a breakfast meeting.

Before then, I had heard only a little about Arnold. In 1967 or '68, Rock Stonewall told me there was a "South African monster" who was sweeping bodybuilding by storm. He said his name was "Arnold something." As it turned out, Arnold's role model was a South African bodybuilding champion and movie star—who portrayed Hercules—named Reg Park. Arnold trained with Reg in South Africa and was featured in the muscle magazines, and Rock assumed that he was South African. Of course, Arnold was from Austria and was known in the magazines as the "Austrian Oak."

**Reg Park as Hercules**

This was not unusual for bodybuilders—to gossip and get the facts wrong—for Rock to assume that Arnold was South African. I mention this because it was so typical of gym talk, where unsubstantiated rumors were par for the course.

I remember when Rock told me that Joe Weider was in the Mafia. "He's one of those rich guys with a dark limo and a chauffeur who waited outside while Mr. Weider surveyed Eaton's Health Food Store," Rock said. He was smiling and genuinely impressed by Joe's supposed gangster persona. It wasn't until later that I got to know Joe Weider, and I found him to be fair, reasonable, and a terrific entrepreneur—not exactly a Mafia don.

At any rate, it was December 1977 when Arnold and I met for breakfast at a hotel on Baltimore's Inner Harbor, just as city officials were starting to develop it. I was twenty-seven, and Arnold was thirty. We stood in line waiting to get into the crowded restaurant, and his body reminded me of Frankenstein, which shows how far I had gotten from my days with Sergio Oliva and Bill Seno.

Arnold was wearing a turtleneck and sports coat. I relied on my reporter's notepad and my near photographic memory for conversations I really wanted to remember. That memory skill made college easy for me because I paid careful attention to the professors' lectures.

Arnold was just becoming famous then. For instance, a woman paid for our breakfast and came over to thank him for inspiring her son to work out, and that night on the local news, I remember an advertisement in which the anchorman said, "A mountain of muscle visits Baltimore today. Details at 11." I watched as the anchorman read my story on the air, pretty much word for word.

The documentary *Pumping Iron* was released in January 1977, eleven months before my breakfast with Arnold, though at that time, I had not heard of it.

During the interview, I did not tell Arnold about my earlier interest in bodybuilding. I let him talk and found him to be fascinating. He kept pointing to his forehead and talking about his "third eye," which was another way of describing visualization, or the process of picturing reaching your goal—feeling what that would feel like.

He was preaching to the choir, as I had long been an advocate of visualization. I remember chain-smoking cigarettes and could tell that this did not bother him at all. I'm sure he was used to it, having grown up in Europe in the 1950s. I did ask if it bothered him, and he said no, he hadn't even noticed.

After our meeting, I wrote an article for a muscle magazine focused on his use of visualization, sent it to him in California, and asked if he could get it placed. He wrote back that he had tried with Joe Weider, but Joe declined, so he got it published in *Muscle Digest* and put me in touch with the editor, Pete Kight, who sent me a check for a couple of hundred dollars.

Two months after that meeting, I gave up cigarettes and have never gone back. I still smoke a pipe for relaxation—one or two bowls a day—and I don't inhale. For me, collecting pipes has become a fun hobby that has led to many friendships from around the world.

I have written two books on the subject and am convinced that the world of pipes offers an antidote to two of the biggest killers of the elderly: stress and loneliness. I realize this is not a fashionable position, but I have always been comfortable following my convictions.

Bodybuilding was not considered fashionable when I started in 1963, and the only time I was really frustrated was after I had abandoned my dreams, conformed to majority opinion, and stopped working out. I was miserable with that decision.

My meeting with Arnold was in December, and I must say that I was inspired to really get back into training. I had quit cigarettes in February and was going to the gym three or four times a week. I knew how to work out because of those three years in my youth when I had trained so hard.

But instead of starting at age twelve, as a prepubescent, I was now twenty-seven, and the natural testosterone in my body made gains a million times faster. Still, I was way too absorbed with my career to view bodybuilding as anything other than a hobby. I worked twelve-hour days as a reporter and editor.

In October 1978, I was hired by the Los Angeles Times Syndicate, and Carole and I moved into a small apartment in Santa Monica, which was only two miles from the original World Gym. There is no question that, subconsciously, I picked Santa Monica because of this. There was a yearning inside of me to become a bodybuilder all over again, but it took three years for me to discover that consciously and to admit it out loud. Wow, did my life change after that.

CHAPTER SEVEN

~ ~ ~ ~ ~

# NOW OR NEVER

When I first visited World Gym on Main Street, I was wearing a sports coat, and the owner, Joe Gold, greeted me and said, "This isn't a health club. We don't have a juice bar or anything."

I said I understood and just wanted to look around. It was pretty intimidating, big guys with heavy weights grunting and groaning. I decided to join for one month. This was in 1978.

I got to know Joe over the years and found him to be both likable and an extremely competent gym owner. His welding skills were special, too. Along with a fellow named Dan Howard, Joe made some of the best weightlifting equipment in the world, with the bars angled just right, the sleeves of the dumbbells slightly thicker than normal, and the benches solid as rock.

**Joe Gold, 1954.** **Joe Gold as he looked when I trained at World Gym.**

Joe Gold was not friendly on the surface; in fact, he enjoyed being gruff, insulting guys, but usually in a kidding way. For instance, I remember when Mike Myers and I were training three hours a day with Bertil Fox, who was on tons of steroids, Joe said, "How come Bertil keeps getting bigger and bigger, and you guys get smaller and smaller?"

I used to tease Joe back, but in a more subtle way. For instance, I remember one Sunday afternoon at World Gym when the photographer and documentary filmmaker George Butler was at the gym. George had made the movie *Pumping Iron* and was something of a celebrity for Joe.

Well, at that time, George was totally into the arctic explorer Ernest Shackleton. He gave Joe a book about Shackleton and was telling him what an incredible hero the man was, how he had saved his entire crew after their ship got stuck in ice in Antarctica. Joe had a glazed look on his face but pretended to be interested. So, after George left the gym, I went up to Joe and said, "Do you know who Shackleton is?" And he replied, like an angry teenager, "Yeah, yeah, I know all about the guy." It was all I could do not to burst out laughing.

My workouts those first few years at World Gym were halfhearted and timid, and I remained focused on my career, working long hours. I remember seeing Arnold at the gym one morning, but I was reluctant to introduce myself again, to remind him of our meeting in Baltimore. When I was at work that day, I was kicking myself for being so shy, so I decided to call him on the phone. "Why didn't you say hello?" he asked. "Of course I remember you, but I never made the connection at the gym."

After that, I saw him occasionally at the gym in the morning, and he was always friendly. I remember that Arnold called me one day to ask if my wife and I wanted to go river rafting with him and a few friends that weekend, and I said we'd love to, but Carole was nine months pregnant and due any day now. Our daughter, Sara, was born on July 24, 1979, so it is easy to date that phone call.

Still, I was not training very hard, and I was traveling a lot on business. I was eating rich foods and enjoying them and drinking a fair amount. Those were the days of the "three martini lunch," or, more likely, a glass or two of wine, followed by another drink or two before dinner. During that year, I was really starting to get fat, and I hated that feeling.

In January 1981, the *Los Angeles Times* offered a Weight Watchers class in the evenings for interested employees, and I signed up. I dropped about twenty pounds of fat during the next six months and started walking everywhere and even jogging eight miles a week.

We were living in a small apartment in Santa Monica, and I was driving a VW Beetle. But Carole always suggested that we save our money for travel, so in July, we went to London on vacation and took a ship called the *Queen Elizabeth II* back to New York.

While on the *QE II*, I was sitting outside, staring at the vast Atlantic Ocean, thinking about how I had wanted so much to build a body like the guy on that *Strength & Health* cover, and what happened? Why did I give up? Why did I assume that lifting weights was a phase for kids and that adults should be fat and lazy? As I sat there, I thought, that is a ridiculous concept. I could work out just like before—with less time but with more knowledge and efficiency.

One person I thought of was Otis Chandler, who was the boss of bosses at the *LA Times*. He had been publisher and was now chairman of the parent Times Mirror Company. Otis was a weightlifter. When he was a student at Stanford, his nickname was Shoulders because his frame was so wide. He even qualified as a shot-putter for the 1952 Summer Olympics in Helsinki, but a wrist injury forced him to drop out. But I knew that Otis loved to lift weights. If he can do it in his fifties, why can't I do it in my thirties?

**Otis Chandler**

These were my thoughts as I was looking out at the unending ocean. I also thought about a bodybuilder named Joe Abbenda, who had won the 1962 Mr. America and 1963 Mr. Universe contests. He looked like such a nice guy. He was heavily muscled, and his image was all over the magazines when I first started reading them.

It was as if my subconscious mind had absorbed those images of champion bodybuilders from that time. What I did not realize was that the muscles I had developed by working out so hard when I was thirteen and fourteen lay dormant in my body, waiting to come out.

**Joe Abbenda**

There is no question that Arnold's making bodybuilding respectable and Otis's commitment to lifting weights were huge in influencing my thinking—in allowing me to give myself permission to go for it. I was thirty years old and still very youthful. I figured it was now or never. I decided then and there, looking out at the vast, empty ocean, that I would achieve my childhood goal within the next five years, no matter what.

CHAPTER EIGHT

~~~~~

# MEETING FRANCO

After we got home, I bought a *Muscle & Fitness* magazine and spotted an advertisement by Franco Columbu. He was a champion bodybuilder, and I had heard that he was a chiropractor with an office in Westwood, which was only a few miles from our apartment in Santa Monica. The advertisement mostly focused on training booklets that Franco was offering, but I called his office and said I didn't want a chiropractor but wondered if Franco designed workout and nutritional programs for bodybuilders. The woman said yes, all the time, so I made an appointment for July 30, 1981.

I did not realize that Franco was in near-peak condition, only a couple of months away from winning the Mr. Olympia contest for the second time. His muscles were huge and in proportion. He was wearing a short-sleeved white dress shirt, and his giant arms looked like they were going to burst through the sleeves. His chest and back were enormous, tapering down to a thin waist. Wow, this was just what I wanted! I felt like I was twelve and seeing Rock Stonewall all over again!

Franco spoke with a thick Italian accent, but I found him easy to understand, possibly because my mother's father, Marion Lombard, had roots in Florence, Italy. He asked me what I wanted to accomplish, and I told him I would like to achieve a bodybuilder's body but in the most efficient way possible.

I never mentioned steroids or other drugs because they never occurred to me, and Franco didn't mention them
~~~~~

because—I was to find out—he believed in hard training and good nutrition above all else, and he looked down on the guys in the gym who tried to get ahead with chemicals. That's not to say he didn't use some type of steroids to compete—everyone did (and they still do)—but Franco was old-school in limiting their use and focusing instead on hard training and good eating. He also placed great emphasis, like Arnold, on the mind.

He wrote down a program for me, and when I asked about nutrition, he said, "Try to eat as many natural foods as possible. If it is in a can or wrapped in plastic, try to avoid it." I learned over the years that his basic diet was Mediterranean—pasta, eggs, fish, lean meats, fruits, vegetables, and nuts. When he was working out hard, he ate a lot because he had a big engine to feed, but when he was not competing, he controlled his intake of food.

My membership at World Gym had lapsed, so I decided to try Gold's Gym in Venice to see if I liked it. They had just moved from Santa Monica, where they had a really crappy storefront gym for a short while. This was after Joe Gold had sold the rights to his name and gym, and after he had closed the original Gold's Gym on Pacific on the border of Santa Monica and Venice—the gym featured in *Pumping Iron*. But the Gold's I joined for ninety days was on Hampton Drive and is still there. In fact, it is the original Gold's Gym for the franchise that became a worldwide phenomenon.

I would work out really early because I had the most energy at the start of the day and because I had to finish in time to get to my office downtown before 9 o'clock. I would get up at five and start working out at five thirty.

I met some nice guys at that gym, and I got pretty good workouts, but I didn't like some things about it. The giant ceilings and barnlike atmosphere, which many people love, were just not for me. Also, in those days, the dumbbells rattled, and I was always afraid they would come loose and knock out some of my teeth.

So, early one morning, I decided to check out World Gym on Main Street, the same one I had joined briefly in 1978. It was something like four thirty in the morning, and there was only one guy there working out. He was doing incline bench presses with 315 pounds, rep after rep. When he stopped, he got off the bench and asked in a deep, friendly voice, "How can I help you?"

I told him I had been training at Gold's and was thinking about switching to World and asked his opinion. "You can't go wrong at either place," he said. "They're both great gyms. But I like this one better. More quiet. Cleaner. No music. Everyone leaves you alone. Joe Gold started the original Gold's and then sold it and left the business for a few years, and now he's back with World Gym."

The place was small, with carpeting and low ceilings, and had the feel of Triumph Gym. It felt like a giant living room converted into a gym. It also had an outdoor gym, which you could use after 7 a.m. The time restriction was because residents lived in houses next door.

The man doing the incline presses with enormous poundages was Steve Merjanian, who was a Muscle Beach legend. Talk about a gentle giant! He could not have been nicer or more welcoming. I pulled out my checkbook and wrote out a check for $150 for a one-year membership. I realize that many people today pay that much every month for their gyms, or maybe for one or two sessions with a personal trainer. The membership price at World Gym in those days was one of the great bargains of the century.

**Steve Merjanian doing incline bench presses at Muscle Beach and posing.**

I worked out that day and became a regular with the early morning crowd. There were only a half-dozen parking spaces under the gym, and I always got one because I arrived so early, usually around 5:30 a.m. You had to walk up a long staircase, and initially, I felt like I was voluntarily going to a prison, where you minded your own business and tried to look as tough as possible. But over the next few months, I started recognizing the same faces and found that most of them were quite friendly.

The equipment was fantastic, and the gym was always kept very clean. I could climb into my own world of peace and quiet—and muscle building—and concentrate on following the program Franco had outlined. This was incredibly helpful, especially because every weightlifter had his own theory and wanted to tell you what you were doing wrong.

Mike Mentzer was into "heavy-duty" training of something like twenty minutes of all-out effort—maximum weights for a few reps. Arnold and others had said the way they built their bodies was through twenty-five or thirty sets per body part, training two hours in the morning and two at night, six days a week.

Franco told me to ignore all the chatter and just follow his routine. He said to work out four days a week for an hour and a half per workout and divide my muscles into limbs and torso, so one day, I would do chest, shoulders, and back—in that order—and the next day, I'd do legs and arms. It was so great to have someone who really knew what he was talking about tell me there was a right way and a wrong way to train. When people in the gym would tell me I should be doing more sets or fewer sets, I just ignored them, knowing I was following Franco's routine.

After a month, I went back to see him at his office. I realize that personal trainers today spend workout after workout with their customers, making suggestions about each rep, but with Franco, it was once a month or once every few weeks for a half-hour in his office. He gave the advice, and you were supposed to follow it.

Not everyone can do that, but at that time and place, with that photo of Guy Mierczuk imprinted in my brain, I was determined to stick with it. I was sitting across the desk from Franco when he told me to stand up and take my shirt off, just as he had done during our first meeting. I did, and I was feeling self-conscious, but less so than I had a month earlier. He broke out into a wide grin. I could tell it was genuine and he was really thrilled.

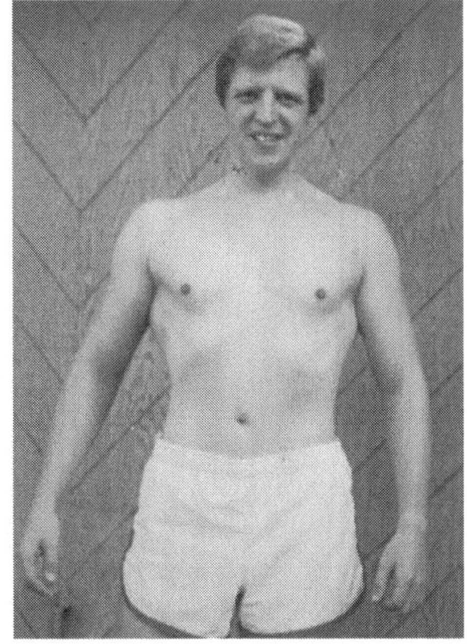

**The first photo shows how I looked when I first saw Franco, and the second photo shows my build after six weeks of following his weight training and dietary program.**

"Unbelievable! I cannot believe how good you look!" he said. "I just don't believe it. I have never seen anyone make so much progress so fast!"

Well, that was it. That was all it took to propel me into continuing to pursue what has become a lifetime of positive feelings about lifting weights. It was as simple as those sentences of praise from someone who really knew what he was talking about and who really meant it.

CHAPTER NINE

~ ~ ~ ~ ~

# FEELING PUMPED

What neither Franco nor I realized was that the progress I was making was not starting from scratch, even though it felt that way. Those three years of bodybuilding, 1963, '64, and '65, at ages twelve to fourteen, had stayed in my body, creating a framework for a thick chest, wide back, strong shoulders, thick arms, and powerful legs. All it took was a few months of regular bodybuilding workouts following Franco's program to activate the memory hidden deep within my muscles.

I left his office feeling on top of the world. I wanted to go straight to the gym and train for hours! I had settled on World Gym on Main Street in Santa Monica as my new gym.

I also traveled a lot on business, and I remember one trip sending me to Boston for a newspaper conference. In 1981, it was not easy finding a gym, especially one that was open at night. I asked the hotel clerk, and he sent me to a downtown YMCA, where the weightlifting gym was in a dark, dank basement. Again, not unusual at that time.

There were mats on the floor, so I lay down on one of them and started doing crunches and leg raises, which Franco had recommended. He said to start with four sets of 25 reps of each exercise, or a total of 200 reps. That was to be followed by two types of side bends without weight, 100 reps each. That made a total of 400 reps for my abs. I did a total of 125 reps and thought that maybe Franco had made a mistake, and I was doing too many reps. But when I asked him about it later, he said no, he meant for me to do 400 reps. That was all I could do that night before becoming exhausted. Today, I frequently do 1,000 reps for my abs, and never think twice about it, but it took years and years to get to that point.

In those early days at World Gym, I tried to block out the other people in the gym and just focus on my workouts, on getting a pump by doing sets and reps with as much weight as I could use without risking injury. That was another interesting difference between Franco Columbu and most bodybuilders. He was super strong—deadlifting more than 700 pounds!—and he told me not to fall into the trap of using light weights and high reps just to get a pump. "You need real

**A young Franco deadlifting a ton of weight! Love that dog, too!**

strength to build solid muscles," he said.

He said it was super important to concentrate on the muscles being worked. "You need to put your mind into your muscles," he said. Still, it was unavoidable to hear conversations in the gym, especially after Arnold arrived. He was loud and fun, always using words like "joy" or "fantastic" to describe things. There was one fellow with thick glasses who had a serious look in his eyes but a slight smile on his face. Arnold would greet him enthusiastically. "Well, it's the Professor! Good to see you today!"

A few months later, I discovered why he had that nickname. I was walking on Spring Street downtown, along the side of the *Los Angeles Times* building, when I saw "the Professor" walking in a suit and tie with two men, also in dark suits and ties, on either side of him. I stuck out my hand to shake hands, and "the Professor" put out both his hands, showing me he was in handcuffs. The FBI agents alongside him kept him moving. So, the next day, I asked some guys at the gym what was going on, and they said he was a professional counterfeiter who had just been busted!

I'm sure Arnold knew nothing of that. He just liked the guy because he was genuinely likeable and clearly very intelligent. He was one of many characters I met in those early morning workouts. Another was the grandfather who had just posed nude in *Playgirl* magazine. We got to know each other, and I discovered he was remarkably conservative. He said he made the decision to pose on a whim and regretted it, especially because he was being hounded by many aggressive older women.

Franco worked out at home, so I told him some of these stories. He would chuckle and then say, "Forget all that. There are so many people at the gym who never make any progress. They just go through the motions. You need to focus if you want to make gains."

In hindsight, I think he was mostly right, but not completely. Even the people "going through the motions" looked better than the ones who never visited the gym. But of course, they were wasting valuable time goofing around when they should have been training. For them, the gym was as much a social setting as a place to exercise. I enjoyed the conversations—mainly observing them but sometimes chatting—but I was always more focused than most, which is another reason I made progress so quickly.

My childhood friend Bob Myers was living in Santa Monica and making a living as an artist. We became friends all over again as adults, and he drew my caricature for my thirty-first birthday, a painting I treasure to this day. In fact, it has been hanging on my office wall for nearly forty years.

Bob was a runner and kept himself in terrific shape. I jogged a little, and he lifted weights a little, off and on. But for him, running was natural, and for me, lifting weights was natural. You have to listen to your body to find out what type of exercise you enjoy most so you will stick with it.

**My thirty-first birthday present from artist Bob Myers.**

Bob had one great observation about the feelings, created by endorphins, that come from going for a long run versus having a strenuous bodybuilding workout.

"When I run, my problems float away," he said. "But when I lift weights, I feel like I can kick down the door and tackle any problem."

That is really profound. I had those exact same feelings. Bob put into words just what I had experienced.

Over the years, I have learned how to create either feeling by lifting weights. At various times, I go all in with bodybuilding workouts, heavy and designed for muscle building, and create that sensation of being able to tackle any problem. At other times, I work out light and nonstop, including five-minute spurts of fast-walking uphill on a treadmill or riding a stationary bicycle, and my problems float away.

These days, I usually do three bodybuilding workouts a week and two cardio workouts a week, all with weights. In all of my workouts, I include twenty or thirty minutes of nonstop training as a way to get cardio benefits, though I keep mixing it up and don't follow a rigid routine. I have learned to have fun during my workouts, and one of the ways to do that is by shocking your body, and shocking your muscles, in a low-impact way. Who knew that the rewards for such a small amount of effort could be so enormous?

CHAPTER TEN

~~~~~

# SETTING SHORT-TERM GOALS

When I go to different gyms today, I am struck by how dependent so many trainees are on their iPhones. You should leave your phone in your car or gym bag.

It is not easy to remember to concentrate on the muscle being worked, but it is immensely helpful for making progress. It is always a good idea to think about what you're planning to do in that day's workout. Sometimes, I even write it down.

Along the same lines, I always write down what I did after each workout. I started keeping a journal in 1981 and have kept that up ever since—week after week, year after year. I store them in boxes and occasionally refer back to them. When I look at my journal from that year, I see that on September 6, 1981, one month after my initial consultation with Franco, I wrote: "My new short-term goal is not to miss a workout (weights or aerobic) during September." Underneath that, I wrote: "Note on 9/27/81 Goal reached."

I also was watching my diet very carefully. After studying a number of diet books, I had determined that I could reach my ideal weight if I limited myself to 2,400 "net calories" per day. By "net," I meant after exercise. So, if I burned up 600 calories in the gym, I could consume 3,000 calories in food, less 600 burned off, which equals a net of 2,400.

**I was watching my diet carefully and really putting on muscle each month.**
~~~~~

I asked Franco about low-carbohydrate diets. I told him about the fellow in the gym who had lost sixty pounds on a zero-carb diet. Franco said, "Zero carbs? You may as well take your brain and nail it to a tree. You won't have any energy. If you want to cut carbs, do so after three o'clock in the afternoon. But before then, eat a fruit plate or pasta or other complex carbohydrates that will give you energy."

On October 29, 1981, I saw Franco again and wrote in my journal, "Franco once again said I look great, and I could tell he really meant it. He said I have much more muscle and much less fat. 'I am really impressed,' is how he put it." I told him that we were going to have a family reunion in Chicago at Christmas and asked if I could make much progress between now and then—a two-month period. "You won't believe how much progress you will make in the next two months," he said. "You are doing everything right."

Setting short-term goals like that was another key to my success the second time around. I think that when I was thirteen or fourteen, I only looked at the long-term goals, and that did me in. Remember those photos I had taken with Rock Stonewall's professional photographer the summer I turned fourteen, when I got depressed because I could not believe how little progress I had made after so many hours in the gym? Well, let's look at them as I wish I had seen them, as I see them now, more than a half-century later. Here is what I would have said to that kid:

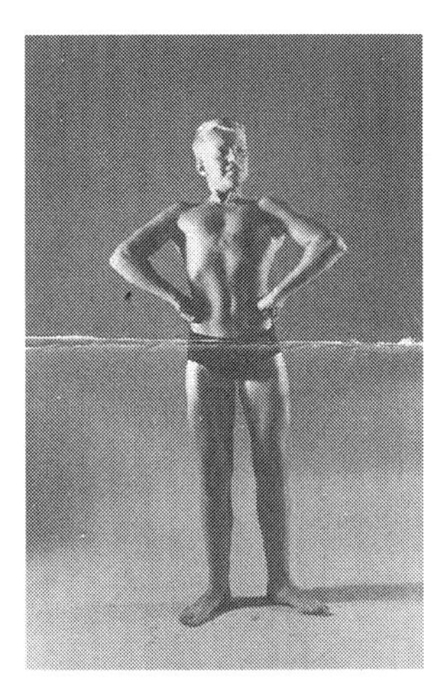

**Photo taken in the summer of 1964, when I was thirteen.**

First of all, I would have said, "What a natural poser! Such a look of confidence—straight back, proud, and heavily muscled for someone between eighth and ninth grade. Unbelievable. You can see how your shoulders, arms, and forearms are starting to develop, not to mention your lats and chest, tapering down to a thin waist and legs that have fantastic potential."

If I could have seen then what I see now, I would have trained twice as hard after seeing that picture! Instead, I saw only flaws. "Can you believe how pathetic I look compared with John Grimek? So skinny and undeveloped. After all those hours in the gym—maybe this isn't for me. Maybe I'm just not cut out to be a bodybuilder."

Then there was the back pose, which today blows me away because of my developing shoulders, arms, lats, and calves, all forming in a nice symmetry and balance. With five more years of steady training and healthy eating, I would have looked exactly how I wanted to look. But I could not see that then. Between my tears, all I could see was that, compared with Joe Abbenda or other champion bodybuilders of that era, I was just a child. Of course, at thirteen or fourteen, I was closer to childhood than adulthood, but I wanted to rush the process of growing up and building my body. In my impatience, I gave up entirely and then had no chance of reaching my goal.

When I look at this picture more than fifty years after it was taken, I see tremendous potential, but at the time, all I could see were flaws. Here is a photo of my back pose taken five years after I started training seriously, making gains very slowly, one workout at a time. If you compare it with the one taken when I was thirteen, you can see exactly where the potential lay within my body, but at the time, I could see nothing but weaknesses, and, thus, I eventually quit.

I would have told that thirteen-year-old kid that you miss one hundred percent of the shots you don't take, and if I stopped shooting the ball, or training in the gym, of course I would miss out on making the gains I wanted so badly. That was a major advantage of being thirty-one and not thirteen. I understood all this and was determined to stick with it the second time around, no matter what.

I started reading the bodybuilding magazines all over again and always found helpful advice. I had a lot of pictures taken during those early years of my second go-round with bodybuilding, knowing they would help me make progress. This was something Arnold, Franco, and the magazines all recommended.

I would set a date three months in advance, make an appointment with a professional photographer, and use that as a motivator for going to the gym and sticking with my diet. I was doing all this while holding down an executive position as vice president and general manager of the Los Angeles Times Syndicate. But instead of the workouts interfering with my business career, they enhanced it. My mind was clear and focused. I had pretty much stopped drinking because of the calories, and I had this great surge of energy all the time, feeling like I was conquering the world.

The only time doubt crept in was when a voice in my head would say the photo sessions were artificial. Who cares what you look like? But another voice shouted back, "I do!" This is something I dreamed of when I was a kid, and I abandoned my dream once, but not now. Not this time. Besides, by making training and healthy eating a part of my life, it became just that—a part of my life.

They say good habits are hard to form but easy to live with, while bad habits are easy to form but hard to live with. Well, I had formed the difficult habit of serious weight training and healthy eating, and it was relatively easy to stay the course.

I worked hard to develop good form with my exercises. I bought some home movies of

Franco training—doing the exercises he had put on my program. I had a friend named Steve Devore, whose company, Sybervision, produced high-quality films. I sent Steve some of these movies, and I will always be grateful to him for sending them back as videotapes showing Franco doing the same exercise over and over. For instance, the film showed Franco doing maybe eight or ten reps of side lateral raises with dumbbells, which is a superb shoulder exercise. The edited video showed Franco doing something like a thousand reps, and I would stare at the television, allowing the correct form to be imprinted on my brain.

On June 5, 1982, I wrote in my journal, "Celebrate!!! One year without missing a workout." But then on June 30, I wrote, "Franco told me to get more serious about my diet." I wondered why he would say that, but I didn't really question it. His advice had been great so far, so he must have known what he was talking about.

Little did I know that he was thinking about asking me to help him with a project he was working on—one that would give me a major league short-term goal, boost my confidence, and propel me on the road to lifting weights my entire life.

CHAPTER ELEVEN

~~~~~

# THE BUSINESSMAN'S WORKOUT BOOK

The next time I saw him, Franco told me he was writing a book for businessmen, and he asked if I would be interested in telling my story for the book and having pictures taken of me doing the exercises he had recommended. I not only said yes but also was very honored!

He said the photos would be taken at World Gym in November, which gave me three months to diet and step up my workouts. During that time, I was training two hours a day, six days a week—not year-round, just for the photo shoot. I treated it as if I were getting ready for a bodybuilding competition.

Frank Zane offered seminars at his house in Palm Springs, which he called "Zane Haven." I signed up and was really excited about spending four or five days with him and other bodybuilding students. Franco and Frank had competed often, and, though rivals, they both respected each other, and Franco thought it was a good idea for me to go.

~~~~~

But then something came up at work. My boss went mountain climbing as a lark and wound up collapsing on the mountain. He was airlifted to a hospital, and the initial diagnosis was a heart attack. Later, that was changed to altitude sickness, but when they thought it was a heart attack, I was told that I needed to be at the office in his absence.

I explained that I had already paid something like $500 for five days at Zane Haven, and that was a lot of money for me at the time. They reimbursed me while insisting that I be at the office. The seminar ran during the week and on the weekend, so I drove to Palm Springs that Friday night, arriving late, and spent Saturday and Sunday there.

That was plenty.

Frank and his wife, Christine, offered all kinds of great advice over the two days that I attended. I remember meeting many nice young bodybuilders, including Laura Combes. I was shocked when I heard a few years later that she had died in her apartment in Florida of acute alcohol poisoning. I was really sad when I heard that because she was such a nice person.

One of the tips I remember Laura giving me was to raise your head when doing leg raises. I've been doing them that way ever since. I remember learning in Christine Zane's meditation session that you shouldn't resist the negative thoughts that come into your mind; simply let them go in and go out; let them float away. I've remembered that ever since as well.

Frank showed me how to improve my form on many different exercises, such as the calf raise, where he recommended standing on your toes for a few seconds periodically while doing calf raises. We all knew to stretch them at the bottom of the movement, but this was the first time I realized the importance of the top. He showed me how to do a concentration curl with correct form and several other exercises that I have profited from for forty years.

What I admired most about Frank and Christine was their inner calm and their close relationship. They really are a wonderful couple, and they inspired me greatly.

Probably the single biggest takeaway I got from Frank concerned diet. He said that watching calories was fine, but if I ever wanted to compete, I needed to cut carbohydrates as well. He suggested that I try a very low-carb and low-fat diet for one week before the photos. I wound up doing it for two weeks and was amazed at how sharp my abs were.

Frank also put me in touch with Rheo Blair, whose protein supplements were used by champion bodybuilders such as Arnold Schwarzenegger and Larry Scott, tennis champ Bobby Riggs, and other star athletes. He lived in a big house in the Hancock Park section of Los Angeles.

When I met him and bought his protein powder, plus some amino acids and other supplements, he complimented me in a way that surprised me: "My supplements are designed to help guys look like you. You already have the look that we promise to give!" I was slightly embarrassed, and did not really believe him, but in hindsight, it was just another example of my own insecurity—not really believing how good I looked.

I also remember that on Sunday afternoon, we all gathered at the Zane's swimming pool for swimming, tanning, and chatting about bodybuilding. When I took off my T-shirt, Frank said, "Wow—are you entering a contest soon? You look ready." I was stunned. I had no idea I looked that good.

In fact, that happened several times at World Gym. One of the most memorable moments was with Steve Merjanian, when I saw him early one day and he said, "You must be getting ready to compete. You look terrific." Again, I attributed his compliment to my suntan and discounted all those hours of hard work in the gym and all that discipline to eat a severely limited diet.

In addition to having dieted to the point of having almost no body fat, I also got a deep tan. I had grown up in Chicago, and, other than that one summer in France, had not had an opportunity to tan much until I came to California. Fortunately, from the point of view of skin cancer, the tanning I did for bodybuilding was pretty limited.

On the day of the photo shoot, the photographer, Bob Gardner, and Franco showed up at the gym, and we did the exercises and had the pictures taken. Bob is a wonderful photographer, and his wife, Gail, is a fantastic partner. They make a great team, and over the years, I worked with them several times more.

The book was called *The Businessman's Minutes-a-Day Guide to Shaping Up*. It sold well at the time as both a coffee table-sized hardcover and as a paperback. Eventually, it went out of print, and I was very excited thirty years later when my company, Creators Publishing, brought it back into the marketplace as an e-book. This allows us to have a digital archive forever—for my grandchildren and Franco's.

Believe it or not, I was thinking of that at the time, thrilled that even if I never picked up another barbell again, at least I could show my grandchildren this book. It was concrete proof that I was a bodybuilder.

In hindsight, those thoughts were rooted in fear—a fear of getting discouraged and quitting again. That's why Franco's constant encouragement was so important. He helped keep me energized for new training programs and reaching new goals.

When I look at the book now, I am struck by how ripped I had gotten. My abs were incredible, especially for a thirty-two-year-old businessman.

But after we took those photos, there was such a letdown. I had set a big goal and reached it. Now what?

CHAPTER TWELVE

~ ~ ~ ~ ~

# PROGRESS

I really enjoyed being in the spotlight in bodybuilding as Franco's star pupil, and I was definitely on the road to reaching my goal of having as much muscle as Guy Mierczuk. I wrote a before and after story for the *Los Angeles Times*, which they printed on December 24, 1982—Christmas Eve.

On the morning the paper came out, I was working out at World Gym, and Joe Gold asked, "Was that you in the paper today?" I said yes, and he smiled and said, "I thought so. I thought that was you," which was his way of offering a compliment.

Then a local TV station called to say they had seen the story and wanted to do a profile of me as an executive who had discovered this fountain of youth. They came to the office to make videos, to our apartment in Santa Monica, and then to World Gym. One of the employees at the Los Angeles Times Syndicate cut out a paper star and taped it to my office door, which I thought was pretty funny.

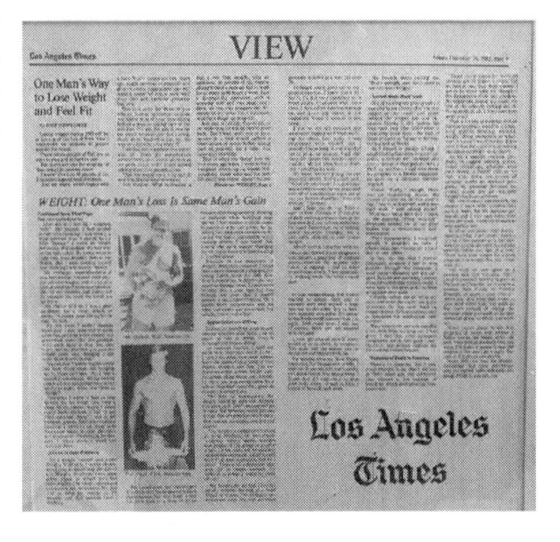

VIEW

One Man's Way to Lose Weight and Feel Fit

*WEIGHT: One Man's Loss Is Same Man's Gain*

Los Angeles Times

By the spring of 1983, I was working out harder than ever, probably two hours a day, six days a week. Every two months, I would have photos taken, usually by Carole, just to see what progress I was making. Of course, the gains slowed down once I had absorbed all the improvements that were a result of muscle memory, but still, I could see progress over time.

Here are two before and after photos that show what I looked like when I first saw Franco and what I looked like two years later:

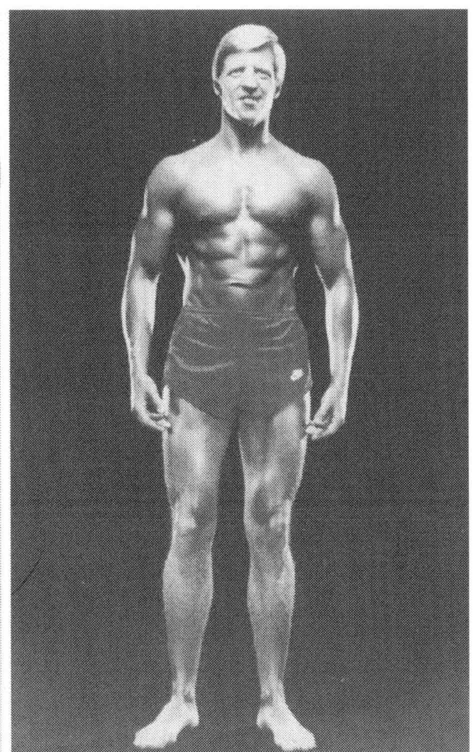

**Franco Columbu was the best coach imaginable.**

I was really settling into a bodybuilder lifestyle, even while holding down such a demanding job. I felt good; I was proud of my physique and enjoyed training and healthy eating. Being a good husband and father were important to me, and I had tremendous energy for my kids when they were little.

Our daughter, Sara, was born in 1979 and our son, Jack, in 1982. Often, after returning home from work in downtown Los Angeles, I would change out of my business suit into workout clothes, put Jack in a backpack and Sara in a stroller, and head out for a three-mile hike before dinner.

**With Sara, Jack, and Carole at our new house in Santa Monica, which we moved into in 1983.**

Going to World Gym almost every day, early in the morning, I would see many of the same people. My training was always focused, and I was not there to socialize, but I do remember overhearing a lot of funny conversations.

There was an undercurrent of homophobia, though it was always masked in humor. It was not unusual for Joe Gold to arrive in the morning to see his gym filled with a dozen macho guys working out—there were very few women in the gym in those days—and announce in a booming voice, "Good morning, ladies!"

There were plenty of other comments along the same lines.

In 1987, one of Creators Syndicate's new columnists, conservative Mona Charen, was on the *Oprah Winfrey Show* to debate the topic of gay marriage with Bob Paris, one of the few openly gay bodybuilders. I knew both Mona and Bob very well—one from business and the other from the gym—and I had enormous respect for both of them.

My own feelings about gay marriage are the same as those expressed by Arnold when he was governor of California—essentially, "Live and let live." It is not an issue I get riled up about.

But in the '80s, I'm not sure if that was my opinion, though I don't remember ever having strong feelings for or against it. I knew that Bob Paris had helped me tremendously in my bodybuilding and that he was someone I grew to admire.

However, I remember the morning after they debated on Oprah's show, I was training hard at World Gym, and Eddie Giuliani, a longtime bodybuilder—and practical joker—asked in a loud voice, "Did anyone see the Oprah show yesterday?" When I said that I had, he said, "Okay, when Arnold comes in, tell him that Bob Paris looked really great wearing an 'Arnold' T-shirt on *Oprah* yesterday when he was promoting gay marriage."

We all thought that was so funny. We knew that Arnold was becoming known worldwide as the "Terminator," and gay marriage was not accepted at the time the way it is now. Although Bob Paris's being gay was the source of the joke, it shows how brave he was to be honest, and all of us laughing would have given anything to have as much muscle as Bob had.

There has always been a gay undercurrent in bodybuilding, though the vast majority of bodybuilders are straight. For many years, bodybuilders felt the need to mock gays as a way to assert their straightness, so to speak. I think it's much healthier now that being gay is more accepted, so some bodybuilders are free to identify themselves as gay, while the majority are straight.

If you read the book *Total Recall*, which is Arnold's updated autobiography, he tells the story of staying with bodybuilding promoter Rolf Putziger in Munich and having to fend off Putziger's advances.

If you look at old bodybuilding photos, many of them appear naked, including the immortal Eugen Sandow.

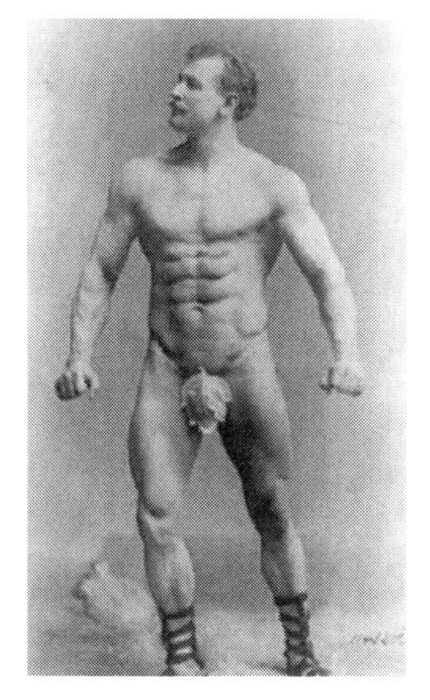

**Eugen Sandow**

I have no doubt that when my dad spent time with Bill Jacobs at Triumph Gym, asking if I would be okay working out alone, he was concerned about homosexuals taking an interest in me. And when Bill said I would be fine, I'm sure he said it with a reassuring but macho tone of voice.

Of course, I never had a clue, and no one ever came on to me.

I do remember one bodybuilder who was training at Triumph Gym for the 1964 Mr. America contest named Ralph Kleiner. I remember that, for two weeks before the contest, his diet was limited to cottage cheese and orange juice. He looked good, though I don't think he placed in the contest. When I would see him training hard, I was always impressed by his muscles. I remember asking him, like the kid I was at the time, to "make a muscle," which meant to flex his bicep, and I remember he had great arms.

But I mention Kleiner because if you look at some of his photos on the Classic Bodybuilders website, it looks like he posed for gay publications. He always treated me with respect, and it never occurred to me that a bodybuilder could be gay. He never came on to me in any way. Some people on the internet have written that he owned Triumph Gym at one time, but I don't think that's accurate.

I had always assumed that Bill Jacobs owned the gym, but it is possible that he was the manager, and other people—two gay guys—owned it. According to a biography of the gay artist Chuck Renslow, Triumph Gym was founded in 1958 by Irvin Johnson. Then, a few years later, the actor Bob Cummings persuaded Johnson to move to Los Angeles, and he introduced him to other celebrities who wanted to take his nutritional supplements. That was when he changed his name to Rheo Blair and became famous within the bodybuilding world for having great supplements.

Johnson sold the gym to Renslow and Domingo Orejudos. They might have wanted to make it a gay gym, but gradually, so many serious weightlifters and bodybuilders signed up that Bill Jacobs, who was straight, was brought in to run it.

If a bodybuilder was gay in those days, there was no way he would tell anyone outside the gay community. It was not until twenty years later that a Mr. Universe announced he was gay.

That was Bob Paris, and he is an incredible person. It took enormous courage for Bob to come out of the closet, and I have nothing but respect for the guy. I got to know Bob really well when I decided to enter my first and only bodybuilding competition, which came a few years later.

**Bob Paris**

Bob helped me with my posing and contest preparation, and I was constantly impressed by his wisdom, insight, and common sense. It was no accident that Bob was Mr. Universe and a strong competitor for Mr. Olympia. He had an amazing physique—incredible size and symmetry—and he is also extremely intelligent and articulate.

But I'm getting ahead of myself. Let's go back to the spring of 1983, six months after I had my pictures taken for Franco's book, when I was training as hard as ever. There was this monster in World Gym named Bertil Fox. He was so heavily muscled and so strong; it was incredible.

He would come in every day with his Jamaican wife, Kim, and I struck up a conversation with both of them one day. I was always trying to learn as much as I could about bodybuilding, and I wanted to study how Bertil was bench pressing more than 500 pounds for reps and how he was doing tricep pushdowns with 300 pounds—the limit on the stack—and seated dumbbell presses with 120-pound dumbbells.

**Bertil Fox**

My brother Robert was living in Los Angeles, and he is a very good photographer. I told him about Bertil and asked if he would be willing to make videos of him working out, and he said, "Sure, it sounds like fun." So then I asked Bertil if we could film him over two days working every body part. I said he could make videos and sell them as training courses.

Bertil said yes, and we were off to the races.

CHAPTER THIRTEEN

~ ~ ~ ~ ~

# TRAINING WITH MR. UNIVERSE

Bertil Fox had won the Mr. Universe title three times before he and his wife, Kim, moved from London to Los Angeles. Joe Weider sponsored Bertil and paid him for endorsements of Weider products.

Weider's headquarters were located in the Los Angeles suburb of Woodland Hills, which is part of the San Fernando Valley, and Bertil's apartment was in Woodland Hills, which is more than twenty miles from Santa Monica. With traffic, that is easily a one-hour drive.

Bertil could have trained at any gym in the city for free because gym owners love to advertise that Mr. Universe chose their gym. And Bertil chose World Gym in Santa Monica as his primary gym. He also trained in the mornings at a gym in the Valley for an hour and a half, doing cardio, stretches, and light weights. But his primary workout, the one he devoted all his energy toward, began at 6 p.m. at World Gym and lasted between two and three hours every night.

On weekends, he trained at World Gym as well, beginning his workout in midmorning and training for three hours on average. He and his massive workout partners were known as "the wrecking crew" because of the incredible weights they moved around.

**Bertil Fox**

The reason I wanted to have a video of Bertil training—a video showing every set and every rep—was to be able to study his form in the privacy of my home. If I missed something, I could rewind the VHS tape and watch it again.

Arnold Schwarzenegger happened to be at the gym when we were filming. I asked if he would be willing to be interviewed, and he said yes. Arnold and Bertil sat on a bench while I asked them questions and my brother filmed it.

**(L-R) Arnold Schwarzenegger, Bertil Fox, and Rick Newcombe**

That was my plan, and I was excited to have the videos. But Bertil had other ideas. He wanted for me to be his training partner.

"The blokes who are with me now don't want to continue," he said, "and I have watched you train, and I see how serious you are. That's just what I want."

I was shocked—and terrified.

"You are bench pressing 500 pounds, and I struggle with 200," I said. "We'd spend the whole workout putting on plates and taking them off. I am nowhere near strong enough to keep up with you."

"Well, we could find one other person who is at your level, so when we do exercises that require barbells, I'll have mine, and you guys will have yours," he said. "And a lot of the exercises are with machines, where you just move a pin to adjust the weight."

As he said this, I looked around the gym and saw this serious bodybuilder doing seated calf raises. I had seen this guy many times but did not know him well. I knew that he worked at a hotel in Santa Monica because a few weeks before, when my friend Joe Novak was visiting from Chicago, we went to that hotel gift shop, and I recognized the man behind the counter as the same bodybuilder I had seen at the gym. We had a friendly chat that night, but two weeks later, at World Gym, I couldn't remember his name.

So, I walked over to where he was seated and reintroduced myself. He said his name was Mike Myers. I told him I could tell he was very serious about his workouts, and I explained that Bertil Fox was looking for two workout partners. He said, "No way. Bertil's way too strong; I couldn't keep up."

I told him that I had said the same thing, and I explained everything Bertil had said about the two bars and using pins. "I think you are stronger than I am," I said, "or maybe we're about the same. But the point is that we only have to keep up with each other and not with Bertil."

He said yes, he'd give it a try. Later, Mike told me the timing was perfect because his training had hit a rut, and he was just thinking about how he needed to do something different—a different workout or a different gym or a different diet.

That brings up an important point if your goal is to stick with a lifting program for long periods of time. You have to mix it up. Variety is the spice of life, and variety is the spice of sticking with a workout program year after year.

This can be as small a change as using barbells more than dumbbells, or vice versa, or using machines or trying different wrist positions when lifting a dumbbell or holding a cable. Another variation is the tempo of your workout—heavy weights and rest between sets versus lighter weights and training with little to no rest between sets. When I do that workout today, I write the word "nonstop" in my journal to indicate that I did a circuit training, or cardio, workout.

**The photo on the left was taken in 1983, when I started training with Bertil and Mike, and the photo on the right was taken in 1986. My gains were slow and steady, and very solid.**

So, we were set—Bertil, Mike, and me—ready to form our own "wrecking crew" at World Gym on Main Street in Santa Monica, the same one I was hesitant to walk into a few years earlier. We would be training with one of the ultimate bodybuilders in the world.

CHAPTER FOURTEEN

~ ~ ~ ~ ~

# GIVING HARD WORK A NEW MEANING

The structure of Bertil's training program was pretty basic for advanced bodybuilding. He trained six days a week, doing chest and back one day, shoulders and arms the next day, and legs on the third day. He would rest for a day and then start the six-day program all over again the following day.

For chest, he would warm up with 135 pounds, which is an Olympic bar with one 45-pound plate on each side of the bar. Fortunately, there were two benches next to each other in the gym, and Mike and I did the same exercise on the other bench. Just like Bertil, we "warmed up" with 135 pounds, which is no warm-up at all! We both eventually got tears in our rotator cuffs, and I suspect those warm-ups had something to do with that.

Then Bertil would ask Mike and me to add another 45-pound plate to each side of his bar, for a total of 225 pounds. He easily banged out ten reps. So far, so good. While he rested, Mike and I would increase the weight on our bar, initially working up to 225 pounds at the end of the workout. After a couple of years, we were benching 275 pounds for reps with just the slightest bit of help from the other.

But after Bertil finished his second set, we would add 35-pound plates to each side, for a total of 295 pounds, and he would do ten reps. Then another 35-pound plate, and he would do eight reps, struggling slightly at the end. Then a third 35-pound plate to each side, and this time, he was dropping to six reps on his own and two more with help from Mike or me standing behind his head on the bench—the way a normal bench press spot would be. Then, finally, we would put a fourth 35-pound plate on each side, for a total of 505 pounds.

Mike would stand on one side of the bar, and I stood on the other. Bertil would do one or two reps and shout, "One off!" and Mike and I would each slide a 35-pound plate off the bar. We had to do this at exactly the same time, with the same amount of strength and balance, so Bertil could hold the bar straight up and be perfectly balanced.

He would do a few more reps and then shout, "One off!" and we would slide off another 35-pound plate. We did this until there were just two 45-pound plates on the bar, which meant that he would be doing a final few reps with 225 pounds.

In between Bertil's sets, Mike and I would do the same thing with our sets, only with lighter weights. Years later, Mike pointed out that we had to work twice as hard as Bertil because we used so much energy to handle his heavy weights, but our weights must have felt like featherweights to him.

So, that was the first chest exercise, five sets of between eight and ten reps. We then did another three or four exercises for the chest, each requiring enormous effort. They included incline bench presses, flat bench flyes, cable crunches, and other similar exercises.

The chest workout took at least an hour, and in the warmer months, it was not unusual for us to have to change T-shirts because we were sweating so much.

Now it was time for back exercises. We would "warm up" with five sets of eight to ten wide-grip pull-ups! Of all the things I am amazed at when I look back to those years, this is the hardest one to believe. I struggle with four pull-ups today, but at that time, I was able to do this exercise fairly easily. Bertil would strap a 50-pound plate around his waist as he did his pull-ups.

**It was not unusual for Bertil to do narrow-grip chins as well as wide-grip pull-ups during different back workouts.**

Then it was barbell rowing. On this one, Mike was almost as strong as Bertil, and I remember that they would be rowing with huge poundages while I used much lighter weights. I had seen too many guys at the gym get sidetracked with back injuries from this exercise, and from T-bar rowing, so I was always a little cautious.

It is interesting how our bodies are all different in terms of strength. In some exercises, such as rowing and squats, Mike was stronger than me, and in others, such as tricep and bicep exercises, I was stronger.

After doing five sets of barbell rows, we would do five sets each of three more exercises, including wide-grip lat pulldowns, front and back, narrow-grip cable rows, and other typical back exercises.

We would end the workout by doing crunches or "Roman chair" sit-ups, where we would all three be talking and rocking back and forth.

But this was a total of 25 sets at *maximum effort per set* for each body part, for a total of 50 sets in one workout. That was chest and back.

We would come back the next day and start all over with shoulders and arms. Bertil would "warm up" with seated presses behind the neck with 135 pounds! When he did seated dumbbell presses, he would start with 80-pound dumbbells and work up to 120s—and, on occasion, 130s. Mike and I would stand at either side of him and hand him those dumbbells. As the weights got heavier, I started rolling the dumbbell up my chest before I was able to hoist it overhead so Bertil could grab the dumbbell handle. One time, I tore a pec muscle doing this.

On the other hand, when it was our turn, all Bertil had to do was grab a 60-pound dumbbell and hand it to us. For him, that was like lifting a paperweight.

We would do 55 sets in total on day two of the week—25 for shoulders and 30 for biceps and triceps (15 sets each). Then abs and calf raises, where he would use the entire weight stack.

On the third day, we would do legs—heavy squats followed by leg extensions, leg curls, leg presses, and lunges. Then we'd do some really intense calf work. I don't remember the number of sets and reps, but our leg workouts were comparable to the upper body workouts, and they were probably even more demanding because of the energy required to do heavy squats.

We trained together during the week for more than a year and on weekends for three years. I made great progress, and I learned how a Mr. Universe builds a championship physique: **HARD WORK.**

Some people try to diminish the achievements of champion bodybuilders by saying that anyone can do that if you take enough drugs. And it's true. Drugs have become an important part of bodybuilding competitions, unfortunately.

But the drugs won't do any good if they are not used in combination with incredibly hard training and healthy eating.

**The new "wrecking crew" at World Gym.**

During this time, I was general manager of the Los Angeles Times Syndicate, and the demands on my time were intense. For many months, I would almost sneak out of the office at five o'clock so I could be ready to start at World Gym at six. It was the main reason, after one year of this, that I told Bertil and Mike I could only commit to weekends.

Mike told me that the people who filled in for me were not the same. They did not have the same feel for his weights and Bertil's, and I found the same to be true when Mike couldn't make it and someone filled in for him.

There was one bodybuilder who started, very excited, as my fill-in during the week. But Mike said that after a short while, he could see the signs of retreat in his eyes.

"We were doing arms, set after set of barbell curls, and I looked over at him when Bertil was doing his set, and I could see that he looked really distant and unhappy," Mike said. "If you could read his mind, he was saying, 'Why did I sign up for this? I don't have to do this.' And sure enough, he started making excuses for not coming to the gym. That happened many times, with many different individuals."

In hindsight, there is no question that we were overtraining, and we would have made better gains doing a lot less. When Joe Gold said, "How come Bertil gets bigger and bigger, and you guys get smaller and smaller?" he was telling us that we were overtraining.

Now, if we had been pumped up with drugs, as Bertil was, it would have been a different story.

I remember once, when we were doing dumbbell pullovers, I was using a 60-pound dumbbell and cheating in my form. Arnold was there, and he took charge, saying, "Rick, that weight is way too heavy for you. Here, grab a 20, and I'll show you good form." He extended the 20-pound dumbbell all the way to the floor and raised it back up. He said to make sure my eyes followed the dumbbell all the way up and all the way down.

I did it his way and could instantly feel the muscles working much harder with the lighter weight. I learned that good form with lighter weights is much better than sloppy form with heavy weights. It is also the way to avoid unnecessary injuries.

**This was me doing pullovers for Franco's book with relatively good form—but at that time, I hadn't learned Arnold's technique of following the dumbbell with my eyes, all the way to the ground and back up.**

There is something called "controlled cheating," where you deliberately swing the weight in order to use heavier poundages, but the key word here is "controlled."

Many times after our three-hour workouts, especially on weekends, Bertil, Kim, Mike, and I would go to breakfast. We also talked by phone during the day once in a while, and I remember Bertil calling me one day when I was at the LA Times Syndicate, and he gave me a number in San Francisco. He was crying, saying that Kim had moved out, and asked if I would call her and persuade her to come back.

I said, "Yes, I'll try." Kim is a wonderful person, and I really enjoyed talking to her. I was sure I could help them patch up their marriage.

But after I spoke with Kim, I told her, "Oh, my God! … Stay away."

## CHAPTER FIFTEEN

~~~~~

# TRAGEDY

At the time that Kim had moved out, Bertil was only a few weeks away from the Mr. Olympia competition, which meant that he was starving himself—no carbs and very few calories.

When Bertil called me to ask for help in persuading Kim to come home, he said, "Oh, man, this is so hard. I can't see straight. I went into a store and saw a granola bar, and I just had to have it. So I ate it, and now I feel like crap. What am I going to do? Kim has to understand the pressure that I'm under."

So I relayed this to Kim and said, "He really needs you, especially as his big contest is only a few weeks away."

With a thick Jamaican accent, she said, "No, mon. It isn't safe. He stabbed me with a fork, and I had to go to hospital, where they gave me nine stitches in my cheek!"

"What?!" I said. "He stabbed you?"

"Yes."

"Oh, Kim, I am so sorry. I know that the dieting makes everyone go nuts, but I totally get it. There is no excuse for that, and no way you can trust him not to lose control again."

I called Bertil back and told him that Kim was adamant, that she was staying with her mother in San Francisco and that she wasn't coming back. I did not reprimand him for stabbing her in the face. I figured it wouldn't have done any good—it would not have changed him—but I decided to be more wary of him.

That said, there were a few times when we got together as friends after that. When they were together, Kim had done all the driving because Bertil did not have a driver's license. I visited him at his apartment on the day he was going to the DMV for his test. He had a booklet that the DMV had given him to study, and he asked me to quiz him. I was amazed at how hard he had studied for this exam and how prepared he was.

As we were talking, he thanked me for making those videos of him working out. I said, "Oh, yeah, I hope you were able to make some money on those," and he showed me a ledger with financial figures.
~~~~~

"Wow," I said, "you've made $53,000 so far. That's incredible!"

I was genuinely happy for him. We drove to the DMV, and he passed his exam.

As the years progressed, Bertil got new training partners and worked out in the San Fernando Valley, and Mike and I continued training together at World Gym in Santa Monica.

We had lunch or dinner with Bertil several times over the years, and he always reminisced about our training together.

"Those were the best years of my life," he said many times.

I think it's true that he looked his best at the 1983 Mr. Olympia contest, when he and Kim were getting along, and Mike and I were his training partners. I kept telling him to smile. Just before he flew to Germany for the contest, I wrote him a letter, saying, "You are built like a monster, and when you smile, you look like Magic Johnson—all charisma." And it was true. If you watch a video of the '83 Olympia, notice how the crowd goes crazy every time Bertil smiles.

At one dinner in Santa Monica, he was telling us a story about traveling in Europe, where customs officials had pulled him aside and gone through his bags. They found all kinds of bodybuilding drugs and confiscated them. He was furious.

"What right do they have to do that?" he asked. "It's none of their business what I put in my body."

Eventually, Bertil moved to Saint Kitts, where he was born, and built his dream house and Mr. Universe gym. He was a celebrity on the island and living what looked like an ideal life.

But the demons that drove him to stab Kim with a fork had come with him. He had a twenty-year-old girlfriend when he was forty-six. One day, he was angry with her and confronted her at a store. Her mother, who was ten years younger than Bertil, was there and stood between Bertil and her daughter. He pulled out a gun and shot and killed both of them, according to the charges.

Initially, after being found guilty, he was sentenced to death by hanging, but eventually, that was changed to life in prison, where he has been since his conviction in 1997. There is an interesting documentary about Bertil on YouTube called *Death and the Bodybuilder.*

**Bertil Fox as shown in the documentary *Death and the Bodybuilder* as he is being led from court.**

One person interviewed in the documentary is Rick Wayne, who was a champion bodybuilder from the Caribbean during the Rock Stonewall era. Rock spoke highly of him, and I had read one of his books, *Arms and Shoulders Above the Rest,* and really enjoyed it.

During the time that Bertil was working for Joe Weider—when we were training together—Rick Wayne was also working for Weider, and Bertil and Rick hung out together.

In the documentary, Wayne says that Bertil never liked white people. In fact, he stated it more emphatically: "Bertil Fox hated white people. He just hated them. He always felt that they were trying to use him."

**Rick Wayne**

I was surprised to hear that. At first, I was offended. My immediate reaction was: My brother and I made all that money for him and didn't take a dime. Mike and I lifted all those weights to facilitate his doing his sets with maximum poundages. We encouraged him so many times and tried to be his friend. What the hell?

But as I've thought about it, I don't really mind. For starters, it is possible that Rick Wayne was exaggerating or projecting. Who knows, and who cares? Bertil would often make blanket statements that he didn't really mean. Second, Bertil told Mike and me too many times to count that we were the best thing to come along for his training at that time.

If I had a nickel for every time Bertil said, "The best years of my life were the times when the three of us trained together," I would recoup the $53,000 that our videos put into his pocket.

Despite Rick Wayne's comments, I feel indebted to Bertil Fox for showing me how the most muscular man in the world trains. *The level of intensity was staggering.* By keeping up with him, even when it was just on the weekends, I learned so much. Also, we really were friends. I liked him a lot and found him to be intelligent and quick-witted. When he was eating and not competing, he was a warm and loving person with a wonderful sense of humor. We became friends as training partners.

Watching the documentary, I felt so bad for the young man who lost his mother and sister. There is no way to bring them back. I also felt sad for Bertil, rotting away in prison. The whole thing was just such a colossal tragedy. There are no words.

CHAPTER SIXTEEN

~ ~ ~ ~ ~

# COMPETING

The earliest bodybuilding competitions are fascinating to study. Eugen Sandow is considered the founder of modern bodybuilding, and he was a judge at all the early contests. Here he is, in a suit and tie (above photo), at a show with some early bodybuilding contest winners.

**This photo shows Sandow (left) and Sir Arthur Conan Doyle (right), creator of Sherlock Holmes, as judges at an early bodybuilding contest.**

Sean Connery competed in the Mr. Universe contest when he was in his early twenties, looking strong and lean, before he became world-famous as James Bond and other memorable characters. I think that is so cool!

There is something natural about wanting to show your muscles after spending all that time in the gym building them up. I was no different.

Of course, when I first discovered bodybuilding, I dreamt of winning all the contests, but since I didn't stick with it as a teenager, I figured that ship had sailed. Although I was working out really hard and in fantastic shape in my midthirties, my business career was my top priority. Training, at this point, was a big part of my life, but still only a hobby.

**Sean Connery in 1953**

**Sean Connery as James Bond in 1971**

During Christmas break in 1985, I remember talking to a friend, Jack Yee, who suggested that I enter an IFBB contest being held in Los Angeles, which was about six weeks away. I thought, "Why not? I should enter one contest, just for the experience." The fact that I was willing to enter a contest on such short notice shows that I was in great condition, especially because of all those workouts with Bertil Fox. But I knew nothing about posing or contest preparation.

I saw Bob Paris at World Gym almost every day, and he trained in a very controlled and disciplined way. I knew that he also was a personal trainer for bodybuilders. I told him that I wanted to enter a contest that was less than a month away and asked if he would be willing to help me prepare—as a personal trainer.

He said yes, absolutely, so two nights a week, he would come to the small house we had recently moved into. Bob was a master poser, and he also knew a great deal about contest preparation.

**Bob Paris**

We picked some music, and he showed me how to glide from one pose to another. He said I needed to get ripped, so for two weeks, I was to eat only for bare nutrition and nothing else. He said a small bowl of oatmeal in the morning was okay, but for the rest of the day, I could eat nothing but salt-free cans of dietetic tuna and water. I would have one small can every three or four hours.

Picture that. Two weeks of eating nothing but tiny cans of tuna and water, salt-free tuna no less. Oh, yes, there was that little bowl of oatmeal (no milk, no raisins, no blueberries, no sugar, and no honey).

He also said I needed to get tan. So I had to carve out time for the sun, and I signed up for sessions at a tanning bed.

Because of the lack of carbs and calories, my energy gradually was depleted the closer we got to the show. I remember one time after an early morning workout, Jim Morris, a former Mr. America and a real gentleman, asked if I wanted to go to the Omelette Parlor for breakfast. That was a great restaurant that many bodybuilders, including Frank Zane, went to often after a workout at Gold's or World Gym. I can still remember my mouth watering as I watched Jim eating his omelette. It looked so good! Especially compared with the tiny bowl of plain oatmeal that I was eating. What I remember most was drinking black coffee. At least that was soothing.

**Jim Morris** **The Omelette Parlor**

We all start lifting weights to put on muscle, and we assume that health and fitness are part of the package. But for the most part, competing in bodybuilding has become the opposite of health and fitness.

I learned this firsthand, and that was the best way to find out.

The yo-yo dieting, leading to near starvation at contest time, and excessive suntanning are not recommended by any doctor for good health.

Then there are the drugs. The top bodybuilders today must take massive quantities of steroids, human growth hormone, and all types of other chemicals that were created to help with specific health ailments but were never intended to be used by people starting out in good health.

That is why I like the Sean Connery picture so much. He looks lean and healthy. Same with the Guy Mierczuk cover photo that drew me into bodybuilding when I was twelve years old.

After working with Bob Paris, I wound up entering two contests within a week of each other. The first one, sponsored by the IFBB, was beyond my level of bodybuilding growth, and I didn't place. Any one of those contestants would have won Mr. America in the old days.

However, there was a fellow at the gym named Joe Sincere (pronounced "Sin-sare-ay"), and he encouraged me to enter the AAU Mr. Los Angeles contest since I was already in peak condition and it was only a few days away. So I did, and I came in third place and was awarded a trophy that has been displayed in my home gym ever since. I'll always be indebted to Joe for his encouragement.

These contests were held in February 1986, when I was thirty-five. They were the only time I competed onstage. My business career was taking off, and I had to integrate my bodybuilding into an incredibly hectic schedule between business and family.

But at this point, working out year after year, bodybuilding had become like combing my hair or brushing my teeth. It's just a part of who I am. Over time, I had become a bodybuilder for life. The program that I follow today is, in many ways, the same program that I was following in the 1980s, only with lighter weights and faster workouts.

I knew that these two contests, held within a few days of each other, would be my only time competing—for two reasons. First, at this point in my career, I was president of the third largest newspaper syndication company in the world. It was owned by Rupert Murdoch, a man I liked and admired, who was a very demanding boss. Second, I knew that if I wanted to continue competing, I would have no choice but to be pumped up with drugs like everyone else, and that was not even slightly appealing to me.

The AAU contest was a great experience, and I was thrilled to come in third place, but winning a trophy paled in comparison to reaching my goal of building as much muscle as Guy Mierczuk. That was what I had wanted since childhood, and I finally had made my dream come true. But that was it—no more competing. I had adopted a bodybuilding lifestyle, and I loved that.

**There is nothing more important than reaching your goals. It reinforces a feeling of confidence and happiness.**

I have spent a lot of time analyzing how I managed to reach this goal, and much of this book explains what happened. The keys can be broken down into eight steps:

- **Inspiration.** It started with the magazine cover that I saw when I was a kid.
- **Reading and videos for motivation**. All those bodybuilding magazines, books, and videos gave me new ideas and kept me motivated.
- **Encouragement from experts.** This started with Rock Stonewall and then progressed to Franco Columbu.
- **The environment of World Gym.** It was so natural to train hard for big muscles at World Gym because the norm was big muscles.

- **Hard work.** The most dramatic example was my time with Bertil Fox, where we went to the max on every set.
- **Making hard work fun.** Arnold and Franco were masters at this. If you hate your workouts, you won't stick with them, but if you love them, you'll keep training.
- **Small victories along the way.** All those photos showing progress offered great encouragement as I reached one short-term goal after another.
- **The habit of daily workouts.** It just became a part of my life, a part of who I am.

But despite my success, it took many years before I came to "own" the fact that I had reached my goal. That came very gradually, over a long period of time.

CHAPTER SEVENTEEN

~ ~ ~ ~ ~

# FROM KNOWING TO OWNING

Maxwell Maltz was a plastic surgeon who wrote the bestselling book *Psycho-Cybernetics* in the middle of the last century. His emphasis was on self-image. Maltz said that he wrote the book partly because of his experience as a plastic surgeon. He said that a patient with a giant nose wanted it to be made normal-sized. So Maltz performed the surgery and made the man's nose look "normal." But instead of being thanked for the surgery, his patient said that it didn't look any different.

So Dr. Maltz showed the man two photos that he had taken—showing his nose before and after—and the man said, "I see the difference, but I don't feel it."

Maltz discovered that this patient was not unique. In fact, it was quite common for his patients to say the same thing—that they *see* the difference but don't *feel* it.

Well, that was me initially, when I had set the goal to build as much muscle as Guy Mierczuk. I would visualize myself having that muscle. Today, with Photoshop available to everyone, it would be easy to put your face in a photograph showing the body of a muscleman. But in the early 1980s, there was only the "airbrushing" of photos, or drawing from scratch, to simulate having reached your goals. If I were starting out today, I would use Photoshop to reinforce my goals—to see myself as having reached them.

I was fortunate to work with artists, and one of them gave me a drawing showing me doing a double biceps pose with the body of a Mr. America. Later, I had a photo taken in which I was doing the same pose. I wasn't there yet, but I was on my way.

By the time I was thirty-five, I had photos taken with the express purpose of showing me that I had reached my childhood dream—the one that I prayed for when I was thirteen. I saw the photos, but I was not one hundred percent convinced. At a core level, I didn't believe that I had reached my goal.

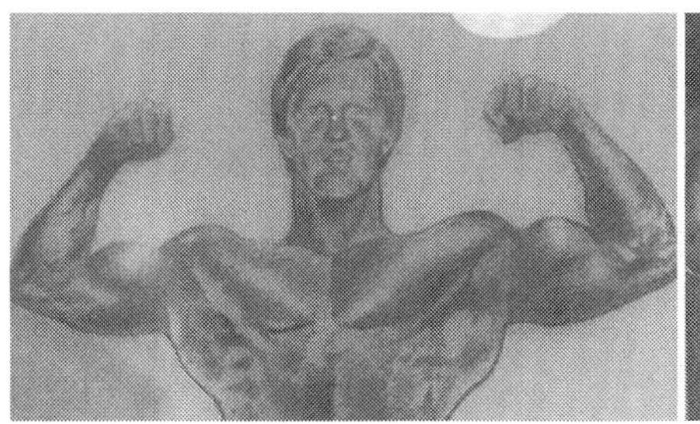

**Using an illustration as visualization (left). The photo on the right was taken in 1983, while the Bob Gardner studio photos were taken in 1986. I kept making gains, slowly, slowly.**

The photos were taken by Bob Gardner at his studio in Hancock Park only a few days before my first competition. Bob Paris met me at the studio that night, and Gail Gardner greeted us at the door. She was friendly and encouraging. The studio had posters of some of Bob Gardner's cover photographs of celebrities for many magazines, including *Shape*, *Muscle & Fitness, Esquire*, and *Los Angeles* magazine.

I had bought aqua blue posing trunks similar to those that Guy Mierczuk wore. I had tried imitating Mierczuk's pose, but it did not highlight my muscles—each body is unique—and, thankfully, Bob Paris took over, suggesting this pose or that. He had me twist one way and then another to best show my physique. Gail offered helpful suggestions, too, and she was an integral part of her husband's success as a photographer of the stars.

I had brought that *Strength & Health* cover from 1963 and showed it to Bob Paris, and he said, "That's nice. It's always great when we reach our childhood dreams."

Wow, I wish I realized that at the time. I wish I had really believed that I had reached the goal. It was only later, after working out year after year, that I finally said, "Okay, I made it."

I've given this a lot of thought, and I think the best illustration is driving a car. You can't learn to drive a car by reading a book about it. There is no substitute for driving a car. At first, you don't believe it. You're actually making this giant machine move along the road, just by putting your foot on the pedal. Each time you drive, you are practicing. I started driving during a summer class in high school, and I got a little more confident each time I drove a car. When I passed my driver's license test, at age sixteen, I thought I was a pretty good driver, but in hindsight, I'm not so sure.

But gradually, over a period of years and then decades, I *knew* that I was a good driver. When I get into my car today, I don't think about driving. It is automatic. I have been driving for many decades without an accident or ticket.

And it was the same with bodybuilding as I continued training over a period of years—a lifetime, in fact. At some point, I came to believe that I really had accomplished my goal. I saw myself as a bodybuilder—not full-time, not competing for titles—but as someone who just loved lifting weights and did it as automatically as brushing my teeth. I was not looking for a "fountain of youth" in my midthirties, but when I was in my fifties and sixties, I realized I had discovered one.

The photo session in Bob Gardner's studio, with Gail Gardner and Bob Paris assisting, was so reassuring in my quest for bodybuilding success. I will always be grateful to each of them for their advice, guidance, and expertise in knowing how to make musclemen look their best.

Here are the photos that Gail sent me after that night in the studio:

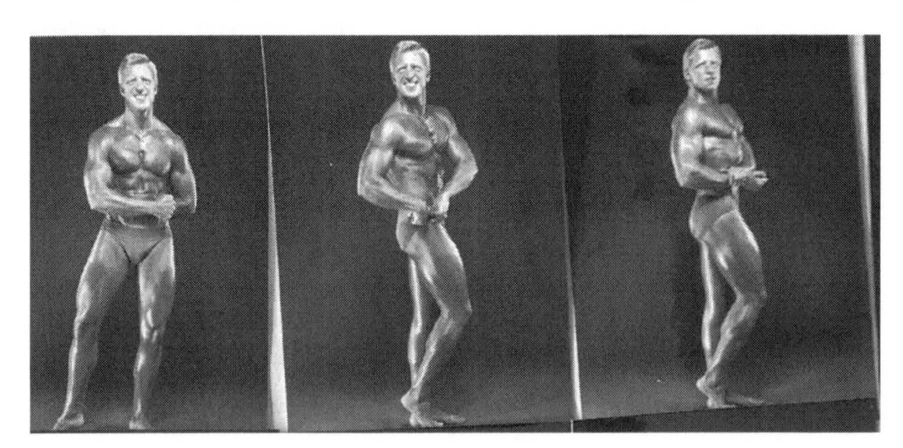

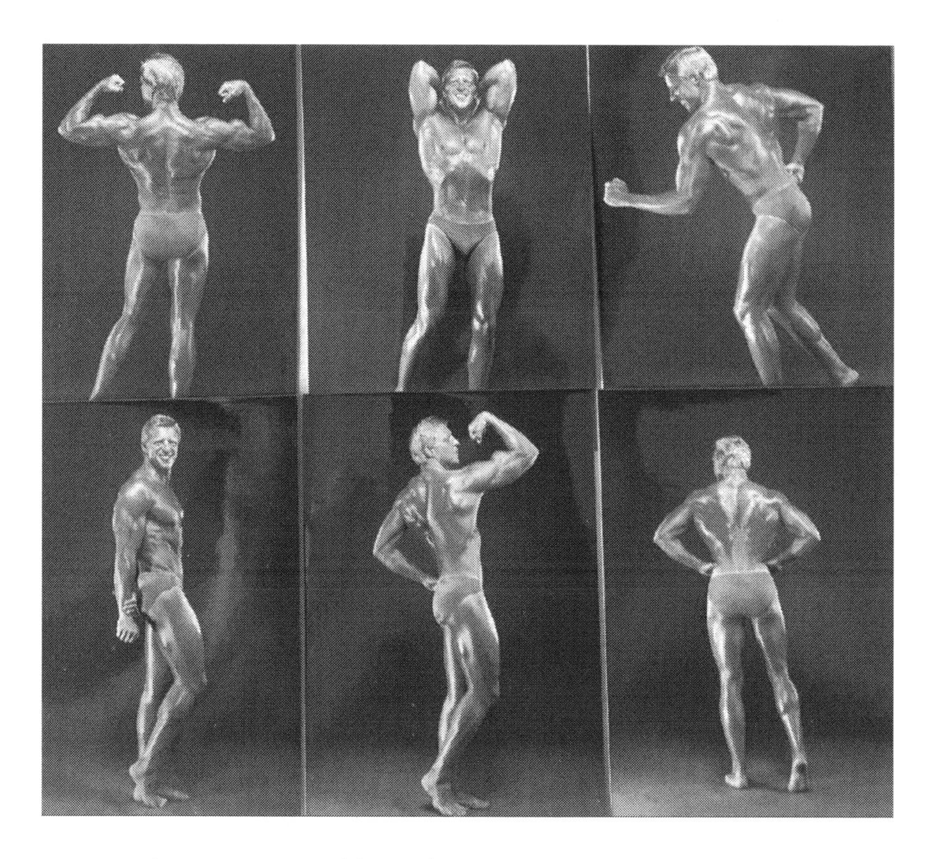

Frank Zane once told me that you need to take a lot of pictures, but you only need the best one or two, where you look really good, and you can throw away the rest. I remember Arnold saying something similar.

After receiving these photos from the Gardners, I sent some of them to Franco, Arnold, and Otis Chandler, and all three were complimentary—effusive in their praise, actually. I chose these three individuals because they were instrumental in my success at reaching this goal. They literally had become my heroes in this endeavor. Without them, I am convinced I would have given up along the way, just as I did when I was fifteen.

CHAPTER EIGHTEEN

~~~~~

# THREE HEROES

As I look back on my initial attempt at bodybuilding—which I regarded as unsuccessful, even though it was not—and my second try—which was very successful, lasting from my late twenties until today—one of the differences was the influence of three individuals who came into my life at exactly the right time: Franco Columbu, Arnold Schwarzenegger, and Otis Chandler.

In 2006, when Carole and I were in Madrid, I sent Franco a three-page handwritten thank-you letter saying that it had been twenty-five years since I first visited his office and gotten on track as a bodybuilder for life due to his sincere, enthusiastic encouragement. I told him he gave me the confidence I had lacked from within.

Franco had a lot of common sense, and many of his observations made a deep impression on me. One time at lunch, we were discussing a mutual friend, Fred Hatfield, who was known as "Dr. Squat" because he broke the world record with a 1,000-pound squat. That was to powerlifting what Roger Bannister's four-minute mile was to running. It was one of those barriers that no one thought possible to break—and then, once someone broke the record, many people followed.
~~~~~

"The human spine is not built to hold 1,000 pounds," Franco said. "I worry about all the powerlifters and bodybuilders who are using so much weight—unnatural poundages because the drugs make it possible—and then later in life, they will suffer the consequences."

I thought of his remarks when I saw the documentary *Ronnie Coleman: The King* on Netflix. Many Mr. Olympia winners and contestants praised Ronnie as "the best bodybuilder of all time," and he comes across as a wonderful man—devoted to his family, a successful entrepreneur, giving back to the community as a Dallas police officer, and, like Franco, one of the strongest bodybuilders of all time. But the film shows Ronnie in extreme pain going up the stairs in his house, one laborious step at a time. He has had so many surgeries, and you can't help but feel compassion for this extraordinary man.

I believe that Franco could have helped him to alter his training so that he would avoid further injuries. I consider myself incredibly fortunate to have had Franco as a coach for so many years. It is the main reason I stuck with my workouts and feel light, limber, and strong in my seventies.

Then there was Arnold Schwarzenegger, who has an amazingly positive attitude. I remember once doing calves with Arnold at World Gym at the end of both of our workouts, and he asked if I wanted to go to breakfast at Patrick's Roadhouse, which is a fantastic diner near the beach in Santa Monica.

We drove there in separate cars. After we were seated, I followed his lead and said, "I'll have what you have." We each ordered a breakfast of eggs scrambled with everything. I remember potatoes, sausage, mushrooms, onions, peppers, tomatoes, and cheese. It was delicious. This breakfast at Patrick's Roadhouse has a very funny story behind it that is part of the restaurant's history as told on its website:

"Arnold was and still is a huge fixture of the establishment. One day when Arnold was eating at his usual table, his mother came into the restaurant and didn't like what he was eating. She pushed everyone aside, went in the kitchen and yelled at them 'I'LL COOK!' She then made him a concoction called 'Bauer Fruhstuck'. This is German for 'Farmers Breakfast.' This custom meal was so gargantuous and distinct that it was later renamed 'The Governator' for easier pronunciation and put on the menu for all to order!"

While at breakfast, Arnold asked me why I was training so hard. After all, I was in my thirties and an executive at the Los Angeles Times Syndicate, and I was training as if I wanted to compete in the Mr. Universe contest. I told him about my childhood dream, and his face lit up when I said the name Guy Mierczuk.

"Oh, I remember Gwee Mierczuk," he said.

Is "Guy" pronounced "Gwee" in German? In his native France, Guy was known as "Gee," with a hard G. But in America, we pronounce the name "Guy," just like we might say, "He is a good guy."

In any event, my explanation made sense to him.

Arnold and I also had lunch at the *Los Angeles Times* in the executive dining room, and I remember telling him that I was so impressed he had come to America only a decade earlier and already owned apartment buildings in Santa Monica and had become a millionaire. I said that I had gone to the finest schools and was succeeding in the corporate world, but I was still driving a Volkswagen Beetle and living in a small apartment.

"I would be afraid to own an apartment building," I said. "What happens if someone's plumbing breaks on a Sunday night, and they call you to complain?"

"That's why I have property managers—to handle those calls," he said. "I don't find out about them until much later."

"But what if someone trashes the apartment, and you are left having to do the repairs?" I asked.

"So you slap a coat of paint on it," he said, smiling.

I also remember him saying, "You know, it's no great mystery how to build a lot of muscles. We know how. Certainly, Franco knows how, and it was the smartest thing you ever did to hire him."

I knew that was true.

I'm sure Arnold doesn't realize how much of an impact his positive attitude had on me. No matter the issue, as I was looking for the negative, he was always finding the positive. I have worked so hard over the years to emulate that way of thinking, and I can tell you now that it really works.

When he ran for governor, I was his most enthusiastic supporter. My company, Creators Syndicate, represents people with widely divergent political views, and I try to avoid taking political sides publicly, but in Arnold's case, I made an exception. It was the only time I have put a bumper sticker on my car: "Arnold for Governor."

**Carole and I attended Arnold's swearing-in ceremony as governor.**

A few years after he was elected, he hit a rough spot and was down in the polls. I wrote an essay talking about how inspiring he had been to me over the years and how he always reaches his goals, which is good news for California. I also sent him this Creators Syndicate cartoon called *State of the Union* by Carl Moore:

When I say that Arnold hit a "rough spot," what happened was this: He had called for a special election in November 2005, and the voters rejected all of his propositions on the ballot. It looked like he was finished as governor. He sent me a letter at Christmastime that year saying that my article, which had been reprinted in many California newspapers, was one of the highlights of his year. He also got a kick out of the cartoon, saying: "If I were writing a letter to Santa today, I don't think I could ask for anything more than the thoughtfulness I receive from friends like you."

Not surprisingly, after encountering the voter setback in 2005, he made a strong comeback and won in a landslide victory in 2006.

One of the many things I admire about Arnold is his quirkiness, which he gets away with because he has such a wonderful sense of humor. He is remarkably charming and funny.

A few years after our breakfast at Patrick's, I remember standing at a very busy intersection in Santa Monica—the corner of 26th Street and Wilshire Boulevard. I had been out for a jog and was wearing a T-shirt and shorts, standing on the corner waiting for the light to turn green. Out of nowhere, there was the blast of a megaphone, saying in a German accent, "Rick Nuu-comb ... Champion Baudy-builder of the World!!!"

I looked up, along with dozens of other people, to see Arnold laughing as he drove his Jeep past me, holding a microphone in his hand.

Another time, at World Gym, I was doing seated incline dumbbell curls, and I heard Arnold say from across the room, "Those aren't natural arms, Rick!" That was the ultimate compliment. It meant my arms were so big they looked like they were pumped up by steroids.

Besides his incredibly positive attitude, Arnold influenced me in another significant way. He showed I could reach my bodybuilding goals while succeeding in the business world.

When I started training at age twelve in 1963, there were no role models of successful bodybuilders who became millionaires. The successful bodybuilders made almost no money from the sport, and the vast majority of successful businessmen had zero interest in becoming bodybuilders. But Arnold served as a role model for me at just the right time—because he had reached both of those goals.

I remember in the 1990s, when I was focused primarily on building Creators Syndicate but still training hard at World Gym, I reread Arnold's early autobiography, *Arnold: The Education of a Bodybuilder*. I was struck by one sentence he had written about his determination and use of visualization to achieve a financial fortune.

He wrote it in 1976, when he was starting to become wealthy, but his net worth then did not compare to the hundreds of millions of dollars he was acquiring in the 1990s. I was so struck by this sentence that I printed it out and illustrated it with a couple of photos of Arnold from the magazines—and put it up on my gym wall, where it still is today.

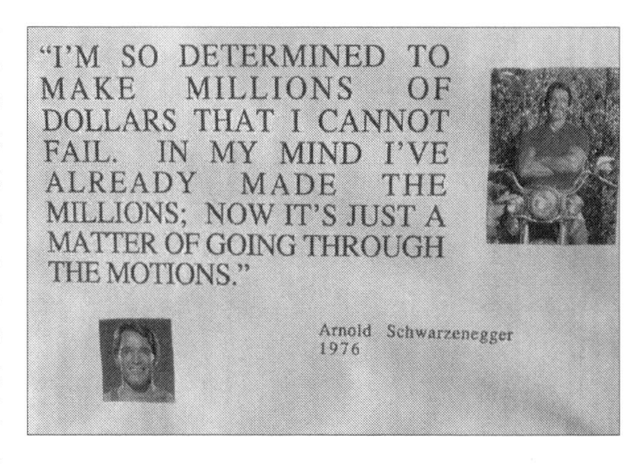


My initial goal was to get Creators to the break-even point, where we would have a positive cash flow. We reached that goal in our third year, and the company has been profitable ever since. Eventually, I bought out all the initial investors, and over the years, we have turned down many offers from media companies that wanted to buy the business. I never want to sell, because I much prefer having a family business that is passed down from generation to generation.

There was one other person who had a major influence on my life at that time. His name was Otis Chandler. When I was hired, he was publisher of the *Los Angeles Times*, and shortly thereafter, he was promoted to chairman of Times Mirror, and Tom Johnson, a wonderful man, became the first non-Chandler to serve as publisher of the paper. One could argue that the Chandler family founded Los Angeles; that's how influential they were. There were the Rockefellers in New York, Marshall Field in Chicago, and the Chandlers in Los Angeles.

**Otis Chandler**

Otis loved to lift weights, and we bonded in the gym. The fact that he was such an enthusiast for weightlifting gave me permission to be one, too. Talk about a perfect setting for me: Instead of being treated as an oddball or someone with arrested development, I was accepted as being a health and fitness nut in an environment where the head of the company was one, too.

In 1979, I was made a vice president of the Los Angeles Times Syndicate, and one of the perks of the job was access to the executive health center. I was twenty-nine, and most of the executives in the gym were in their forties and fifties. There was only one serious weightlifter, and that was Otis.

**Otis Chandler was a serious powerlifter, as you can see by the poundages he was using when in his midfifties.**

The first time I worked out at the *Times*'s gym, I remember seeing Otis doing squats with 315 pounds, which is an enormous amount of weight for any age, but pretty much unbelievable for a man in his fifties. Picture three manhole covers on each side of an Olympic barbell.

I remember feeling excited and totally relaxed, like a kid at recess. This was a stark contrast to being in meetings, wearing our business suits, ties, and white button-downs with starched collars.

"Wow! You really are strong," I said. "Can I give you a spot?"

"Absolutely," he said. "I think you're the first person who has asked me that question in this gym."

A "spot" is a weightlifting term to describe one person helping another to make sure the weights are handled safely and to the maximum ability of the person doing the exercise. That was the beginning, and we spotted each other many times during the next few years.

Competition was in his blood, and one day, Otis announced he was entering a masters powerlifting championship. He trained hard doing bench presses, squats, and deadlifts, and his total poundages were at a world-class level. But a week before the contest, he pulled a hamstring muscle and had to back out. "This reminds me of hurting my wrist before the Olympics," he said.

Another time, I mentioned that we were starting a health and fitness news service at the syndicate, and Joe Weider, the famous bodybuilding magnate, was coming in for lunch.

It was during lunch that Weider told us he was thinking of starting a women's fitness magazine called *Shape*. Otis told him to go for it, predicting a big success. As it turned out, that magazine became a cornerstone of the powerful Weider publishing empire.

I loved Otis. He was such a wonderful person, so unique, and, like me, struggling to individuate from the confines of what was expected of him—and he succeeded at everything.

After I started Creators Syndicate, Otis told me he always had a soft spot for entrepreneurs. He said he had tried to set up the *Los Angeles Times*, and then Times Mirror, so that the executives felt as if they were operating as entrepreneurs. I told him he had succeeded, and it was one of the reasons I felt prepared to start my own business.

In 1997, I sent Otis a copy of the 1984 *Muscle & Fitness* article about him that Joe Weider put in his magazine after our luncheon. I told him we were setting up an employee gym at Creators Syndicate, and I had framed the article and put it on the wall for inspiration.

Otis replied in a letter: "I am still working out regularly but the musk-ox hunting accident has taken care of any heavy lifting except for deadlifts and squats.

"I turn 70 this Sunday. Maybe I'll do some senior competition in lifting."

He also wrote, "It was good to hear from you again, my friend."

That was Otis: friendly, competitive, curious, always exploring new worlds and new possibilities, always seeking new challenges.

One night, after a hard workout, we were in the jacuzzi at the *Times* gym, which he had built for the executives. Otis told me he had met Arnold Schwarzenegger the night before at a Hollywood party, and he liked him very much. This was long before Arnold was a household name.

Otis compared him to Steve Reeves, who was one of the few bodybuilders to become rich and famous in the 1960s. Reeves played Hercules in the movies.

**Steve Reeves as a bodybuilder and as Hercules.**

"There is something charismatic about Arnold," Otis said. "I wouldn't be surprised if someday, he becomes more famous than Steve Reeves."

Talk about an understatement, considering that Arnold was the No. 1 box office star in the world for many years—before becoming governor of California.

After I had left the *Los Angeles Times* to run Rupert Murdoch's News America Syndicate, I remember being invited to lunch at the exclusive Regency Club in the Westwood section of Los Angeles by Gordon Reece, who, at the time, was working with Armand Hammer and his Occidental Petroleum Corporation. Gordon was a political strategist for British Prime Minister Margaret Thatcher and had been knighted as Sir James Gordon Reece.

So, here we are at the Regency Club, surrounded by distinguished-looking captains of industry in Los Angeles, the men and women who owned and ran the city. Picture elegant table settings, the finest china and cutlery, meals served by white-gloved waiters—and me, seated across from Sir Gordon.

The good news is that Gordon was a charming man, dressed in a Savile Row suit and tie, and as I sat across from him, dressed in a Brooks Brothers suit and tie, I couldn't help but think of the ridiculous disparity in our daily schedules. In a few hours, I would be at World Gym, with its gorilla weightlifting logo, working out like a maniac with the massive Bertil Fox.

I remember, at that moment, thinking of Otis Chandler and Arnold Schwarzenegger—feeling confident that they had been in similar situations and that they were probably the only two people in the world who would understand my feelings at that precise moment. At least, the only two who I knew.

As I look back forty years later, having reached the goals I set for myself as a bodybuilder and an entrepreneur, I realize that it was Franco, Arnold, and Otis coming into my life at just the right time that helped make this possible.

I had no idea then that it would lead to this feeling of having discovered the fountain of youth for my seventies and beyond.

CHAPTER NINETEEN

~~~~~

# A BRIEF HISTORY

As a bodybuilder for life, I have read more books and magazines on the subject than you can imagine, including about bodybuilding's early history. I always found it motivating—I still do, in fact—to read stories that inspire me to keep training.

The first bodybuilder from the old days who I had paid attention to was Eugen Sandow, who was famous at the turn of the last century. Yes, he spelled his name without an "e" at the end. His real name was Friedrich Wilhelm Mueller, and he was born in Prussia. He was always referred to as being German, and his birth name was German, but the city he was born in is now called Kaliningrad, Russia. Later in his career, he settled in London, where he died and is buried.

**Posing next to a statue of Eugen Sandow at the York Barbell Museum, in York, Pennsylvania, where they display one of Sandow's original dumbbells with a spring inside, shown below.**

Sandow was known for being a strongman as well as a bodybuilding poser. He was promoted by Florenz Ziegfeld of Ziegfeld Follies and was a sensation at the Columbian Centennial Exposition in Chicago in 1893, known for his posing routines. Later, he was filmed by Thomas Edison's company doing some of those posing routines, and they are amazing. You can find these on YouTube. I recently bought one of his books on my Kindle, and it is fun to read.
~~~~~

The Mr. Olympia contest, which is the highest IFBB award in bodybuilding, features a small statue of Eugen Sandow as the trophy. There is a great biography called *Sandow the Magnificent*, by David L. Chapman, that I highly recommend.

Then there was a man named Alan Calvert, who founded the Milo Barbell Company in Philadelphia in 1902. He wrote books and training courses as well, and he published *Strength* magazine.

In 1932, Bob Hoffman bought Milo Barbell and renamed it York Barbell Company. Hoffman also founded *Strength & Health* magazine—the same one with Guy Mierczuk on the cover.

But before Hoffman, there were a couple of other heavyweights in the bodybuilding world. One was Bernarr Macfadden, who published *Physical Culture* magazine. There is a wonderful biography of Macfadden by Mark Adams called *Mr. America: How Muscular Millionaire Bernarr Macfadden Transformed the Nation Through Sex, Salad, and the Ultimate Starvation Diet.*

The book is fascinating and shows the many ways in which Macfadden, who spent his unhappy childhood in Missouri and Illinois, was the first and most prominent Made-in-the-USA advocate of muscle building, physical fitness, and fasting—all trends that became popular a century later.

Macfadden made a huge amount of money—many millions of dollars. But he also suffered a series of setbacks as the years passed. He relished being famous as an eccentric. He was known as a media mogul who carried forty pounds of sand on his back as he walked barefoot in New York City or played tennis in bare feet. At home, he liked to go around nude, and more than one critic said he had holes in his head. Still, he did much to advance physical culture.

One of Macfadden's ventures was to sponsor a contest at Madison Square Garden called "America's Most Perfectly Developed Man" in 1922, and the winner was Charles Atlas. In fact, he so dominated the competition that Macfadden decided to cancel any future contests because, as he said, "What's the use of holding them? Atlas will win every time."

**Bernarr Macfadden on the cover of his *Physical Culture* magazine.**

By the time I was a teenager in the early 1960s, Charles Atlas had become an institution, with his full-page ads in the back of comic books, the most famous featuring a "ninety-seven-pound weakling" at the beach who has sand kicked in his face by a bully who walks off with his girlfriend.

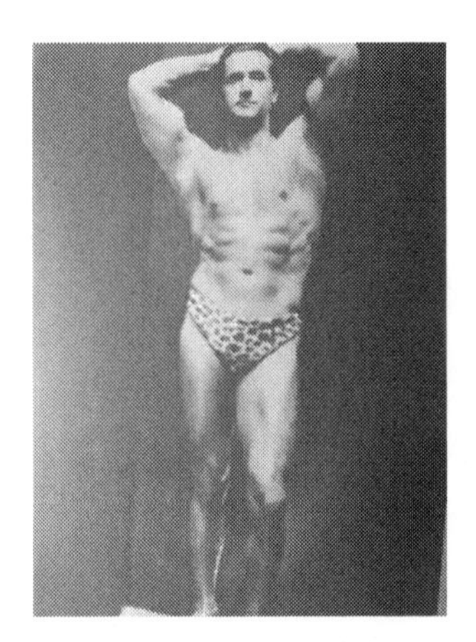

**Charles Atlas**

Charles Atlas promised that if you took his course, you would build muscles and be able to fend off the bully. However, Atlas did not actually recommend lifting weights, even though he had lifted a lot of them in his early years. He said he made his greatest gains by practicing "dynamic tension," which is a form of flexing the muscles over and over and pitting one muscle against another. He said he developed his system after watching a lion stretching.

**John Grimek had an incredible physique and was a masterful poser.**

In the 1930s, '40s, and '50s, the York Barbell Company dominated the weightlifting scene, with John Grimek and Steve Stanko emerging as star weightlifters and bodybuilders. Grimek stayed active until his death in 1998, at the age of eighty-eight.

There is a terrific book about York Barbell and Bob Hoffman called *Muscletown USA* by John D. Fair. Fair chronicles Hoffman's rise in the physical culture world, with special emphasis on Olympic weightlifting, which was Hoffman's passion. Fair takes us from Hoffman's childhood to his incredible successes in the world of weights to his death at the age of eighty-six. The book is rich in history, told in a friendly way, and I couldn't put it down.

In 2017, Carole and I visited the York Barbell Museum, and that was so much fun. I really felt like I had died and gone to heaven! If you have been lifting weights and want to study the history of physical culture, you won't believe how fantastic this museum is.

They also have a great gift shop, where I bought some T-shirts. I took a lot of photos:

**Standing next to a giant statue of Bob Hoffman (left). The sign says, "PLEASE DO NOT LIFT THE WEIGHTS" (middle). I love this statue of the immortal John Grimek (right).**

Meanwhile, Joe and Ben Weider of Montreal challenged Bob Hoffman with their bodybuilding contests and muscle magazines. Eventually, they became the gold standard for bodybuilders. Ben traveled the world promoting bodybuilding contests, and Joe moved to California and founded some of the most successful bodybuilding magazines in history. He also founded an exercise equipment company and a health food supplement business. When he finally retired, Joe Weider sold his magazines and fitness equipment business for hundreds of millions of dollars.

On July 9, 2007, I was honored to be in Sacramento to help celebrate what Governor Schwarzenegger had designated as "Joe Weider Day." Many of the top bodybuilders from the old days were there, and it was a unique opportunity to chat with Franco Columbu, Sylvester Stallone, Christine and Frank Zane, Laree and Dave Draper, bodybuilding writer Dick Tyler, photographer Bob Gardner, and Bob's wife, Gail. There was a luncheon at the Statehouse, where Arnold and others paid tribute to Joe, and later that same day, there was a more casual dinner in Sacramento.

**With Betty and Joe Weider celebrating "Joe Weider Day" in 2007.**

There is a movie about Joe and Ben Weider called *Bigger*, which I enjoyed, though it was ridiculously harsh on Bob Hoffman. I think even Joe would have conceded that it was an unfair portrayal of a very tough competitor, who he managed to overtake, but only after many decades of hard work.

Dan Lurie was a promoter who published muscle magazines and appeared on television to promote bodybuilding. He once was invited to the White House and famously arm-wrestled President Ronald Reagan in the Oval Office.

There was also a man named Peary Rader, an early bodybuilder and Olympic weightlifter, who founded *Iron Man* magazine with his wife, Mabel. John Balik and Mike Neveux bought *Iron Man* from the Raders and turned it into a hardcore bodybuilding magazine. What I remember about those *Iron Man* magazines from the early 1960s was the smaller format and fantastic covers of musclemen, but then inside, they devoted a lot of print to what I thought were boring statistics about weightlifting. Remember, I was thirteen. Reading them now, I am impressed by how many great articles they had about training and nutrition.

**John Balik**

I met John Balik at Franco Columbu's memorial service in Santa Monica in October 2019. We both paid tribute to Franco. We sat at the same table at dinner, and he and his wife were lovely people.

One book I read when I was in my early teens was called *The Book of Strength,* and it made a deep impression on my young mind. It is long out of print, but I still have my copy, fifty years later. I just looked it over to see why I enjoyed it so much.

For starters, the writing is exceptionally clear, and I felt like the author was talking directly to me when he wrote that the book "contains a message of good cheer. You can get strong. Not only that, but you can *look* strong. You can increase the girth of your chest, broaden your shoulders and build up your calves and thighs. All these are worthy ambitions; don't ever let anybody tell you otherwise."

The author was William Lindsay Gresham, who wrote the novel *Nightmare Alley*, which became a 1947 film noir starring Tyrone Power. It is a cult classic today. Gresham was married to the poet Joy Davidman, and the couple had two children. She became famous after their divorce, when she married C.S. Lewis, who wrote about their relationship in the play and movie *Shadowlands.*

What I liked best about Gresham's approach to bodybuilding was his nurturing and encouraging tone, plus his conversational writing style.

In recent years, a powerlifter named Brooks Kubik has written the *Legacy of Iron* series of novels about the early days at York Barbell, and I just love them! He captures the youthful enthusiasm for getting big and strong that so many of us felt as teenagers. He brings old-time musclemen such as John Grimek to life, and he pays tribute to Bob Hoffman.

**Brooks Kubik's *Legacy of Iron* series of novels is fun to read and motivational for training.**

It is unfortunate that the only time I met Hoffman, he was eating lunch and understandably wanted to be left alone. Brooks portrays Hoffman as the hero he was in terms of advancing weightlifting and bodybuilding in America. Brooks also has written books about weightlifting and powerlifting that are terrific, especially for older lifters. He advocates "dinosaur training," which is as old-school as you can get.

There is also a terrific website called Oldtime Strongman, run by John Wood, that offers many old magazines and training manuals. There you'll find names like Sig Klein, Earle Liederman, George Jowett, Professor Attila, and George Hackenschmidt, among others.

**Earle Liederman**

**George Hackenschmidt**

Bill Hinbern is a world-famous weight training authority, author, collector, and publisher of Strongman memorabilia, books, and courses. He has a website called Super Strength Training, and I have found it very profitable to subscribe to his free newsletter, which has motivating articles and offerings.

Terry and Jan Todd were world-class powerlifters who have written about the history of strength training. They have set up a giant collection of books, videos, and training courses about physical culture at the University of Texas in Austin, where they were both professors. Another physical culture historian who I always enjoy reading is David Webster of Scotland.

The brilliant Charles Gaines wrote the classic bestseller *Pumping Iron*, with photos by George Butler. Gaines also wrote the novel *Stay Hungry*, which was made into a movie starring Arnold Schwarzenegger, Jeff Bridges, and Sally Field. In addition, he wrote *The Life and Times of Charles Atlas*. I am always inspired to work out after reading Charles Gaines's insightful observations about weight training, which he started doing as a teenager.

The pioneers of lifting weights and, in the case of Charles Atlas, flexing muscles made it possible for me to begin my lifetime journey of discovering the magic of lifting weights.

I was fortunate that the bodybuilding magazines of the old days showed mostly drug-free bodybuilders. Even the ones who used steroids used them in extremely limited quantities, especially compared with today.

The bodybuilders who I most admire are the ones who trained for years and years and ate a healthy diet. Some were more genetically blessed than others, such as Guy Mierczuk. Zabo Koszewski was another example of someone with good genes who loved working out more than anything. They had different physique structures, but each made the most of what he was born with.

**Two of my all-time favorite bodybuilders were Zabo Koszewski (left) and Guy Mierczuk.**

There is so much good about lifting weights as practiced by these pioneers, and I just love reading their stories. They still motivate me to keep working out.

CHAPTER TWENTY

~~~~~

# HOME GYM

Once I reached my bodybuilding goal, my new goal was to continue training hard while taking my business career to a new level. Bodybuilding really helped lay the foundation for success in business in that most of the motivational techniques that I used to build my body were the same ones I used to build my business.

My goal was to switch from being a successful corporate executive to a successful entrepreneur, which may not sound like much of a change, but it really is. Whatever structure I had in my business life I had to create.

In January 1987, I founded Creators Syndicate and for the next few years was working day and night, though I always managed to continue training. We helped revolutionize an industry with some of the most talented cartoonists and columnists in the country. Johnny Hart, the brilliant creator of the comic strips *B.C.* and *Wizard of Id*; Ann Landers, the enormously popular advice columnist; and Herblock, the legendary *Washington Post* editorial cartoonist, all helped make Creators possible.

William Randolph Hearst had founded King Features Syndicate in 1914, and they owned all their comic strips—the names, characters, and likenesses. Several cartoonists had filed lawsuits over the years, against King and other syndicates, and they all lost. I thought this was inherently unfair, so Creators became the first major syndicate to allow cartoonists ownership rights to their work.

My success in reaching my bodybuilding goals helped give me the fortitude to challenge an entire industry. It took an enormous amount of courage, and I was widely denounced—condemned even—by industry leaders. Being strong and fit helped anchor me, knowing that, since I had reached the goal of building as much muscle as Guy Mierczuk, I could withstand the criticism and mockery of my competitors.

The more they tried to put us out of business, the more successful we became, and eventually, Creators became the third-largest syndicate in the world. Also, we forced the industry to change;
~~~~~

today, all the major syndicates grant cartoonists ownership rights to their work.

As I was approaching my forties, becoming financially independent became more important to me than bodybuilding. One required my full-time commitment, while the other became a hobby, something I had learned to do and pursued regularly, not so much to build bigger muscles but to stay in shape as I was approaching middle age.

At around that time, Joe Gold moved World Gym from Main Street in Santa Monica to Abbot Kinney Boulevard in Venice. Many people said they liked it much better, but not me. I missed the close environment of the Main Street gym.

But I also wanted to build a home gym, mainly to save time. I wouldn't have to commute to the gym, find a parking space, work out, shower, dress, and drive home—all of which took precious minutes that I was devoting to building the business.

Our family had bought a new house, and I converted the garage into a gym so I could have indoor/outdoor workouts. The weather is so beautiful in Southern California that I did—and still do—some of my training outside. I went to a store that sold equipment and bought a squat rack, benches, dumbbells and racks, Olympic barbells, plates—you name it. I bought a Nautilus calf machine that can also be used to do squats, dips, and chins.

Another piece of equipment that I added was a leg extension and leg curl bench, which I bought from Larry Scott. He was a great salesman and a sweet guy, though I remember asking him if the apparatus came fully assembled or if I had to set it up. He said there was no set-up required. When it arrived, I was sure he misunderstood me, because it was in parts that had to be put together. Still, it was worth it. It is a wonderful machine for working the quads and leg biceps.

That's the amazing thing about having started as a kid, when every piece of equipment was such a treasure. Now, as an adult, I can buy whatever I want, and I think back to how excited I would have been when I was first starting out. Being deprived early really helps you appreciate the equipment.

As for working out at home, I have a theory about privacy and wealth, which is that having money is good, because you can buy privacy, but having too much money is risky, because you can lose your privacy if you're not careful.

When I was poor, everything I did was public. I took public transportation; I swam at public pools; I worked out at public gyms; and there were a hundred other things in my life that were public. But once I started earning more money, I could buy privacy, as in a private car, a private home gym, and—this being Los Angeles—a private swimming pool.

But a new problem arises if you get too much money. You lose your privacy! Instead of driving yourself, you are driven by a chauffeur. You might have a home gym and swimming pool, but typically, rich and famous people have dozens of workers at their houses at all times.

I remember once visiting a very wealthy friend in Orange County who had just bought a $20 million mansion near the home of the late, great Kobe Bryant—someone I had met at World Gym when he had first moved to Los Angeles as a teenager and was working with a personal trainer. He was kind and friendly—just what you'd expect.

The friend who I was visiting was selling his business and contemplating retirement. When I was at his house, which overlooks the ocean, I was greeted by the butler. Then three different women came into the room at various times to see if I wanted something to drink. When we walked past the kitchen, there were a number of cooks working away.

"How many employees do you have inside the house?" I asked, and I just about fell over when he said, "Seven."

"Okay, so what happens when you wake up in the morning and want to go to the kitchen to get a cup of coffee?" I asked. "I sleep in a T-shirt and pajama bottoms and would not want an audience before my first coffee."

"Oh, I just push a button, and they bring the coffee to my room," he said.

I remember thinking it's good to have money so you can buy privacy, but not so much that you lose your privacy.

I found that I loved training at home, in seclusion. I did not have to block out conversations at the gym. I never had to wait for someone to finish a set before using the equipment I needed to use. I love training outside so much that I lose track of time. I can train for two hours, and it feels like five minutes. Time flies when you're having fun.

That's how I judge gyms these days—not by the equipment or music or anything else—just by the clock. If twenty minutes feel like two hours, it is a terrible environment and a gym to avoid. If time flies when you're working out at a different gym, that's the one to stick with.

There are so many great gyms these days, especially compared with when I first started training. In those days, there were a handful of bodybuilding gyms, plus the YMCA dungeons, and Vic Tanny health clubs in cities across the country. But today, the choices are many, and that makes training—and finding the right gym for you—easier. Remember my clock test. The best gym is the one where you don't look at the clock.

**My home gym today.**

In 1999, we moved to an area that was like a park, and I was able to build a new indoor/outdoor gym in our garage. I loved it instantly! One of the things I like best is that we have total privacy. The garage is tucked away behind a long driveway, far from the street.

Bill Pearl has always been an inspiration to me, and I read about his incredible home gym at his ranch in Oregon. He calls it "The Barn," and he even has T-shirts for his guests who train with him that say, "I Survived The Barn." For many years, Bill has started his workouts every day at 4 a.m., which is too early for me. But I can handle 6 a.m., get a great workout, and feel invigorated all day as a result.

**Bill Pearl's home gym, which is housed in a converted barn on his ranch in Oregon.**

There is something so peaceful and soothing about working out as the sun is rising, listening to the birds chirping and greeting the day before all the noise and buzz of activity begins. I just love that quiet time. I have seen skies that were purple, orange, and pink at different times.

When I was in my fifties and having my annual physical exam with Dr. David Boska, our family doctor, he asked about my workouts. After I told him, he said, "That's great, but you should start using lighter weights. You can do higher reps if you want, but the key is to preserve your joints and to have maximum flexibility as you get older." He actually started saying this when I was in my forties, and it took a long time before that sunk in, and I will always be grateful to Dr. Boska for his persistence.

In every workout, I go for a pump, but I do so by resting less, doing more supersets and tri-sets, and maybe using a heavy weight only on the final set of a body part. And my definition of "heavy" today is comparable to the weights I used to warm up with thirty or forty years ago.

Vince Gironda once said that he wished the poundages were filed off all the weights so we never knew how much we were lifting. That way, we would pick weights that felt right, and we could then concentrate on good form.

Gironda was amazing and someone I truly admire because he was as opposed to drugs in bodybuilding as I always have been. He built a fantastic physique, and it was all natural. His diet was a little whacky—dozens of eggs every day, heavy cream with protein powder, and almost no carbs. That probably explains why he was so cantankerous.

I saw him greet Joe Gold once at a Los Angeles bodybuilding contest. He was wearing his trademark buckskin coat, and Joe was wearing his trademark World Gym sweatshirt. They shook hands, and neither would let go first. In fact, they started a sort of tug of war, pulling their arms back and forth. I'm not sure how it ended, but clearly there was a lot of animosity mixed in with surface friendship. I think today we would call them "frenemies."

**Vince Gironda**

But both those guys—Gironda and Gold—contributed greatly to the world of bodybuilding. Gironda had theories about weights that were controversial but helpful to many. He disdained the basics like bench presses, squats, and sit-ups. He recommended exercises like dips, hack squats, and preacher bench curls, and he also created the crunch, which is a major advance in the physical culture world.

Joe Gold was not known for creating exercises. He created exercise equipment. He was a welder, and his dumbbell handles were out of this world. They were thick with ridges and super comfortable in the hand. His pulleys and bars had just the right touch. Many of the most successful exercise equipment manufacturers managed to create bars and machines that duplicated Joe's creations.

In the late 1990s, I brought a friend who was a welder to World Gym with me. Joe had moved the original World Gym a third time, taking over an old Sizzler restaurant in Marina del Rey. My welder friend had brought a tape measure, a legal pad, and a pen. The iPhone camera had not yet been invented. I showed him the dumbbell handles, a certain pulldown machine, and various bars that Joe had made and asked him to make notes so he could duplicate them in his workshop so I could use the equipment in my home gym.

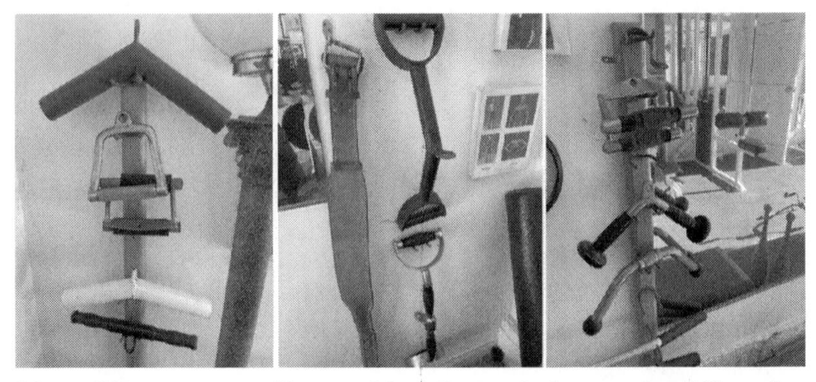

**Many different types of bars and handles work the muscles differently.**

After ten minutes, he came up to me and said he was all set, so we left. He then spent more than a week duplicating the equipment, and I have been using it ever since.

When Franco put his hands around the handles of the dumbbells in my garage gym, he wondered if Joe Gold had made them; that is how fantastic they are! I took some photos, which show the thickness of the handles. I had them made for 15, 20, 25, 30, 35, and 40 pounds.

The nice thing about home gyms is that you can keep making improvements. I have added a Cybex Smith machine for my home gym and moved the original squat rack to our office gym. The lat pulldown at my home gym was made by Flex. We also have one in the office gym that I bought from Larry Scott, who sold wonderful equipment.

**In addition to a home gym, we have an office gym at Creators that I use several times a week.**

The point of all this is to illustrate how working out has become such a part of who I am that, over a period of forty years, I have invested a lot of time and money into creating workout environments that make lifting weights as enjoyable as possible. We have large mirrors in both gyms—not for the sake of vanity but so I can check my form and progress as I exercise.

It is easy to succumb to negative self talk, so I am consciously aware of this and always on guard for it. The more you give yourself positive self-talk about your workouts and progress, the more you will succeed at working out, and the more progress you will make.

Along the same lines, the most important issue is not whether you work out at a home gym or a public gym. The most important issue is to create a mental zone for training. In that sense, even at a public gym, you will be in your own gym, focused solely on your own muscles and your own goals. Forget everything else, and enjoy the magic of the pump.

CHAPTER TWENTY ONE

~ ~ ~ ~ ~

# I FINALLY TALKED TO GUY MIERCZUK

In 1992, something happened that really boosted my ego and reinforced my image as a bodybuilder—albeit one who focuses on training and nutrition as a hobbyist and not a professional.

The editor of *Muscle & Fitness* magazine, Tom Deters, called to say that he wanted to interview me for a story about using the principles of bodybuilding to build a business, which was what I was doing. Tom told me that he would be near my office to give a lecture about bodybuilding at Loyola Marymount University. I attended his talk and was so impressed by his knowledge of training, nutrition, rest, and everything else having to do with working out.

We had lunch afterward and hit it off right away. When the story came out, I felt very honored. Joe and Ben Weider were working tirelessly to lift the status of bodybuilding, and my employment with Rupert Murdoch, at the *Los Angeles Times,* and then with Creators Syndicate were no doubt the reasons they wanted to profile me in the magazine.

MUSCLING IN ON SUCCESS

Bodybuilding put Rick Newcombe's physique – and business career – on the fast track to success

By Tom Deters, DC, Editor in Chief

In the same way that I admired them for being committed to bodybuilding and to becoming successful entrepreneurs, they liked the fact that I had been training so hard for so many years and was simultaneously syndicating some of the country's best-known columnists and cartoonists.

I also found them very easy to talk to, and each one was remarkably intelligent. I remember being in Joe Weider's office eight years earlier when someone rushed in to say that Jim Fixx had just died. That was in 1984. Jim Fixx was the poster child of running to prolong longevity. His writings on the subject had been read by millions, especially his signature book, *The Complete Book of Running*.

Everyone in the fitness world was shocked. We thought running and working out would help us live forever, and Fixx was only fifty-two when he collapsed of a heart attack while on his daily run.

Joe and I were alone in his office, and I asked him if this shook his belief that exercise prolonged longevity. "Not at all," he said. "It's like an assembly line of cars, where you have ninety-nine cars that are fine, and the hundredth car is a lemon. Well, that's what happened here. God made a hundred people, and ninety-nine of them start out with a strong heart, but the hundredth is a lemon. Jim Fixx's heart was that lemon."

What is fascinating is that several years after Fixx's death, Dr. Kenneth Cooper, who wrote the bestselling book *Aerobics*, studied all the autopsy and medical reports on Jim Fixx and concluded that Joe Weider was basically right. Fixx's father had suffered a heart attack at thirty-five and died from a second heart attack at forty-three. In other words, father and son were born with weak hearts. If anything, the exercise that Jim Fixx did prolonged his life so that he outlived his father by nine years.

How did Joe Weider know this in an instant, without any medical training and without seeing the autopsy results? That is what I mean when I say that he was exceptionally smart.

I also got to know Ben Weider, who was equally intelligent. I remember having breakfast with him at the Beverly Wilshire Hotel to discuss his writing a syndicated newspaper column for Creators, which ultimately appeared in many newspapers around the world. He wrote that weekly column for a decade before passing the baton to Joe

Weider. Joe continued the column for a number of years after that, working with his editor, Shawn Perrine. Some of Joe's columns were published in a Kindle book called *Ask Joe Weider.*

When we were at breakfast, Ben asked me how I got started as a bodybuilder, and I told the story about Guy Mierczuk. I wondered aloud whatever happened to him. Ben wrote down the name and said he'd check. Later that day, I got a call from his assistant, who told me that Guy Mierczuk ran a gym in Monaco, and she gave me the address.

After the *Muscle & Fitness* article was published, I sent a copy of the magazine to Guy Mierczuk at his gym in Monaco, telling him my story and thanking him for being the spark that got me started. As it turned out, there was an American in his gym that day who was fluent in French. Since Mierczuk did not speak English, and my French isn't too good, the two of them called me at my office. Through the translator, we had a nice chat.

The translator was a personal trainer from Malibu who had been flown to Monaco by a wealthy client who wanted to make sure he stuck with his workouts while traveling. He took a photo of Guy Mierczuk, and I could tell that he had stayed in great shape all those years later.

In subsequent years, Carole and I traveled the globe but never went to Monaco. We visited France many times and stayed in many different cities, and we talked about visiting Monaco, but we never did. I was sad to read that Guy Mierczuk died in 2015 at the age of seventy-eight.

**Guy Mierczuk in his gym in Monaco in the early 1990s.**

I always figured that there was plenty of time to meet him, but I was in no hurry at all. I think, at some level, I was afraid that meeting him would be a letdown. I did not want to know if my hero had clay feet. When I thought about it, I remembered a college professor in an English literature class quoting

D.H. Lawrence: “Trust the tale, not the teller.” I was happy with the inspiring image of Guy Mierczuk posing in front of the Roman ruins, and I wanted to leave it at that. As one friend told me, “He stayed perfect in your mind.”

One other person I sent the *Muscle & Fitness* article to was Bill Pearl. Every time I read about Bill Pearl’s lifestyle, I was motivated to train harder. I loved picturing his home gym and the way that he got up early and worked out hard as a way to start the day. Frank Zane also had a fantastic home gym in Palm Springs, and he, too, liked to train early in the day.

Bill hand-typed a letter in reply, and I was so thrilled by his comments. He said that he loved the story about me and wished the muscle magazines would do more of that type of reporting—about average guys who make great gains by hard work. “I am sure that this article will act as an inspiration for a lot of people who find themselves in the same position you did a few years ago,” he wrote. “I personally believe articles like this have a great deal more impact on our sport than a BIG ARMS article about a champion bodybuilder.”

I had bought the paperback edition of Bill Pearl’s *Keys to the Inner Universe* more than forty years ago and have studied the illustrations many times to find new exercises and to improve my form. Bill Pearl is the personification of all that is good about lifting weights.

About ten years later, he published his autobiography, *Beyond the Universe*, and I absolutely love it. Like Otis Chandler, he is a car collector. Bill also collects rare bicycles. He has many hobbies, besides working out every day. He has such a positive attitude and is so encouraging to others.

My favorite story in the book was his description of visiting J. Paul Getty at his estate in Surrey, England, several days after the 1967 Mr. Universe contest organized by the National Amateur Body-Builders’ Association, which Bill easily won. Getty was in the front row, though Bill didn’t know that. His partner, Leo Stern, helped shield his eyes during a strength performance at the show in which Bill blew up a hot water bottle until it exploded. Bill said that as everyone was leaving the theater, an elderly gentleman jumped up and shouted, “Bill Pearl is king! Bill Pearl is king!”

That was J. Paul Getty, and not long afterward, Bill, Leo Stern, and bodybuilder Craig Whitehead, M.D., were in Getty's limousine being driven to the estate, where they spent one night. It was a sixteenth-century, three-story castle with seventy four rooms.

"Mr. Getty remained a thoughtful host to the end of our visit," Bill says. "After we signed his guest book, he showed us to the front steps and stood waving goodbye until we saw him become a small figure in the distance."

**Bill Pearl and J. Paul Getty in 1967.**

Reading Bill Pearl's story was so inspirational, and every time I reread a section of the book, I am motivated to keep training harder than ever.

Being in contact with both Guy Mierczuk and Bill Pearl were highlights of my journey as I have continued to work out, week after week, year after year.

CHAPTER TWENTY TWO

~ ~ ~ ~ ~

# TWO FRIENDS

I met so many interesting characters at the gym over the years, and there are two who I stay in touch with regularly: Mike Myers and Jack Yee. They are both still training hard. That means they have been working out consistently for forty years each. It's good to have friends who share your hobby. They help keep you on track.

During the Bertil Fox years and afterward, Mike and I trained together for more than a quarter-century, so we learned to read each other's minds when training and spotting. He knows exactly how much lift to give me, and vice versa.

There was a period when Mike worked in sales at Creators Syndicate, and we would train in our office gym. My brother John also joined us at those workouts and has been lifting weights ever since.

**Mike Myers at our office gym in the early 2000s.**

Mike's journey as a bodybuilder was similar to mine in that he started as a teenager, inspired by the magazines. He moved to Santa Monica just so that he could train with the champions.

I'm not sure where he got his work ethic from, but he works out as hard as anyone in the gym, day after day, year after year. And the most important point is that he loves it. I told Mike about this book and asked what he thought of *The Magic of Lifting Weights* as a possible title. He said that would be perfect because "magic" is just the right word.

"Magic is exactly what lifting weights is," he said. "When I was young, around thirteen or fourteen years old, I was skinny as a rail, malnourished, and very weak. At about that age, I discovered weightlifting. It changed my life forever! Through weightlifting and proper eating, I discovered that I could completely change my health and appearance. I am healthy and energetic, all accomplished through the magic of lifting weights. It's that simple."

Mike started out wanting to win bodybuilding contests but at some point concluded that it was lifting weights, not getting trophies, that was the greatest reward. "I realized I didn't have the genetics to be a champion, but that didn't matter," he said.

What mattered was the feeling of blood rushing into the muscles, pumping up, and the feeling of relaxation after a hard workout. These are feelings like no others. There is simply no other way to get those feelings.

I asked Mike what lifting weights and the bodybuilding lifestyle have brought to his life, and he said, "Everything that is good." He stays in great health and says that hard workouts are never drudgery for him. "Working out is a wonderful, joyful, and fulfilling activity. It really is magical."

When Mike and I trained together at World Gym, we chatted occasionally with some of the well-known bodybuilders. I remember that Lee Haney trained in a very dedicated manner, yet he was always smiling and in a good mood. It was hard not to look up to him, and it was no surprise that he achieved so much success.

Tom Platz once told Mike that he admired the way Bertil Fox, Mike, and I were training. "That's how I wish everyone trained," he said. Tom was an inspiration to all of us, especially when it came to doing squats, which is probably the best overall exercise, in my opinion.

**Tom Platz**

Mike moved to the Buffalo, New York, area and trains at a World Gym there. When he enters the gym, there is a big picture of Joe Gold on the wall, and he gets a kick out of the fact that most people don't know who that is. Mike was one of Joe's favorites. Joe called him "the Rocker." That had nothing to do with music; it was because, between sets, Mike would sit on a bench, bend forward a little, and gently rock up and down. In fact, one time between sets, when Mike was rocking, a woman asked him if he was Jewish. She explained that his swaying forward and back was known as shuckling. I think Mike's rocking was to relieve nervous tension, and I'd bet anything that he still does it.

**Mike Myers is youthful in his sixties because of lifting weights.**

Jack Yee started working out at World Gym when he was a student at the University of Southern California. I remember meeting him one day in the outside part of World Gym on Main Street. He was outgoing and friendly, and I could tell that he was smart. After graduating from USC, Jack moved to New York to study for his master's degree at NYU.

That was around the time when I was working for Rupert Murdoch and had to travel to New York one week a month for business. I trained initially at Mid City Gym, which was owned by Tom Minichiello, who reminded me of Joe Gold. He ran a nice gym, though it was nothing like World Gym. He was quiet most of the time but always on the alert to make sure no one was doing anything wrong.

Along the same lines, I remember once training at Sergio Oliva's gym in the Rogers Park neighborhood of Chicago in the 1980s, and he had the funniest signs all over the gym: **"DON'T EVEN THINK ABOUT DROPPING THE WEIGHTS!!!"**

One day when I was working out at Mid City, I saw Rock Stonewall doing dumbbell bench presses with heavy poundages. I couldn't believe it! We hadn't seen each other in nearly twenty years, but he had been so important and inspirational to me in those early years. He was my role model, so helpful, and I loved this man!

**Rock Stonewall doing bench presses with 85-pound dumbbells.**

Rock told me that he had moved to New York and was running a health food store in the city, which I visited later that day. We had dinner that night and caught up on the old days in Chicago.

**Reunited with Rock in the early 1980s at a health food store in New York.**

So, when Jack Yee moved to New York, I told him about Mid City Gym and Rock Stonewall. He got to know Rock, though a short time later, Rock moved to upstate New York, where he died ten years later at age fifty-four from a neurological disorder that was aggravated by steroid use. The Associated Press ran an interesting story about Rock, with the headline, "The Long Struggle of Rock Stonewall."

Rock was a natural bodybuilder for many years, but at some point, he decided to take steroids to become more competitive. "Once you get on them, you get used to the size and that feeling of power and strength," he told the AP. "You see your body explode, and you want to stay like that. You have to keep taking them to maintain the size."

At just the same time that Jack Yee arrived in New York, Tom Minichiello retired and closed his gym. Jack found the Natural Physique Gym, which was much closer to NYU, and when I visited

New York, I trained there many times and enjoyed the atmosphere—until it changed.

The guy who founded the gym was very nice and married to a wonderful woman. I can't remember her name, but she was both attractive and kind. One time, I arrived at the gym when it was just starting to snow. By the time I finished training, the snow was like a blizzard, and I was about to leave the gym to walk back to my hotel with a bare head. She insisted on giving me a knitted stocking cap that was in their lost-and-found box, and I was very grateful.

But later, the owner met a female bodybuilder who was very strong and extremely masculine. I never saw his wife at the gym again. The whole atmosphere changed, with a lot of shouting, so I stopped going there.

I do remember being in New York and going to a bodybuilding contest called "Night of the Champions." I went with Jack and a few of his friends from the gym. I'm not sure how Ben Weider knew I was there, but I was very surprised when he announced that there was a distinguished visitor in the house, "Rick Newcombe of the Los Angeles Times Syndicate." The auditorium, which was packed, had been darkened as Ben was making announcements; a spotlight shone on me, and I stood up and waved. This was totally unexpected, but I was flattered. Of course, what Ben loved was the fact that someone from the *Los Angeles Times* was at an IFBB show.

Over the years, Jack Yee has given me many great health suggestions, my favorite being the Buteyko breathing method. Konstantin Buteyko was a scientist from Ukraine who started out treating children with asthma in Russia and eventually treated the elderly with chronic obstructive pulmonary disease and all types of people in between with breathing issues. The main technique is shallow breathing through the nose, and once I started practicing this technique, my allergies all but disappeared. Prior to that, I had chronic allergies.

Jack has kept up his training, though he has a different workout from Mike and me. We follow the more traditional bodybuilding plan, such as Arnold's or Franco's or Bill Pearl's or Frank Zane's, while Jack no longer does body part training. He practices extreme intensity interval training combined with working on the mind to overcome adversity.

In fact, he is so passionate about his system that he wrote a book about it called *Mental Toughness Training* by Jackson Yee, which is available on Kindle. Jack and I had lost contact for many years after he moved to Massachusetts to pursue his teaching career, and it was his book, which Creators Publishing released, that brought us together again.

Though we have different approaches to working out, it makes no difference. We both are passionate about lifting weights in our own way, and we stay with it year after year. Like Mike, Jack looks young for his age, no doubt because of his working out and attention to diet.

**Jack Yee is lean, strong, and fit at fifty-seven.**

CHAPTER TWENTY THREE

~ ~ ~ ~ ~

# WORLD GYM

When I look back at all the characters I met at World Gym and Gold's Gym, the ones who impressed me most are the ones who continued training their entire lives. One of my favorites was the manager of World Gym, Irvin "Zabo" Koszewski.

Zabo was friendly to everyone as long as you didn't ask him to do anything. He was known as "Mr. Abs" when he competed because of his extraordinary abdominal development. He would do sit-ups on the "Roman chair" in the gym for thirty minutes or longer, gently rocking back and forth, and we all copied him. I have been looking for years for a similar Roman chair but have not been able to find one. I'm sure Joe Gold made it just for Zabo.

One day, when we had both finished our workouts and were getting dressed in the downstairs shower area, Zabo went off on the subject of steroids. He told me that I was making real progress and that, no matter what, I should not take steroids. I had no intention of taking them, and I asked him why he brought that up. He said it was because he had seen so many young guys like me over the years, who trained hard and were determined to build bigger muscles, and he had seen them succumb to steroids to accelerate their progress.

**Zabo on a magazine cover in 1954 and in a black and white photo taken ten years later. He loved to train and stayed in shape his whole life.**

"They make artificial gains," he said, "and then they eventually quit training altogether. That sucks. I hate it. Steroids are ruining bodybuilding, and I wish they had never been invented." Imagine if he saw all the drugs now!

Another time, very early on a Monday morning, he arrived at the gym with his ten-year-old daughter, who was waiting for her mother to pick her up. She was very sweet, and after she left with her mom, I told Zabo that she was cute as a button.

Zabo said he had two girls, and they meant the world to him. He must have appreciated the fact that I was kind to her in that intimidating environment (especially for a ten-year-old girl) because we became a lot closer after that.

Eddie Giuliani was another manager at World Gym, and he was energetic and funny, but when it came to training, which he did every day in the early morning, he was very serious and dedicated. I was always inspired by how hard he worked. One morning, he started singing the song "Sherry" by Frankie Valli and the Four Seasons, and I remember Eddie could hit the same falsetto notes that Frankie Valli was so famous for.

**Eddie Giuliani**

Eddie told me that the hardest workout he ever had was with Jack LaLanne, who was a legend in the health and fitness movement. He opened the first modern bodybuilding gym in America in 1936, when he was twenty-one. The gym was in Oakland, California. He went on to become a television star with his daily exercise program, aimed especially at housewives.

Jack was full of life and energy, and he was an eternal optimist. He also was something of a fanatic, Eddie said, when it came to his morning workouts. There was virtually no rest, and Eddie said it was an experience he never forgot.

**Dave Draper**

**Robby Robinson**

Along the same lines, Eddie said one of the hardest workers in the gym that he remembers was Dave Draper, though by the time I joined, he had already moved and no longer trained at Gold's or World. Eddie said that Dave would train at the old dungeon in Santa Monica in the pitch black with no lights on. I can't remember if he said Dave lit one candle or several, but the point was to create a world of total concentration.

Robby Robinson was a bodybuilder who Mike Myers and I both admired. He worked out hard and kept to himself; he was quiet, determined, and an incredible inspiration. What a build! The one time Mike competed in a contest, Robby helped him prepare and was incredibly supportive.

Before I joined World Gym, I was training at Gold's, and I met two bodybuilding legends: Lee Haney and Mike Mentzer.

I remember working out early one morning, when it was still dark outside. I was near the fence, and I heard someone whispering, trying to get my attention: "Hey, buddy, open the gate, will ya?" He was an enormous bodybuilder with a friendly grin. I did, and he was really happy. I later learned that was Lee Haney, who went on to win Mr. Olympia many times. I think he didn't want to come through the front door and get hassled by someone at the desk who might not have known him.

The irony is that today, every Gold's Gym in the world would pay Lee Haney to train at their gym because he has become known as one of the greatest bodybuilders of all time. In addition, he has trained many pro athletes, including Evander Holyfield and Gary Sheffield.

**Lee Haney**

Lee served as chairman of the President's Council on Physical Fitness and Sports when Bill Clinton was president. I love his philosophy of bodybuilding, which is to "stimulate, not annihilate." He is a devout Christian, which he talks about a lot, and a wonderful man.

When Bertil Fox, Mike, and I were training at World Gym, Lee Haney and his equally strong training partner were alongside us, doing their own exercises. More than a few times, I loaned Lee my lifting belt, and he was always very appreciative. I truly admire Lee Haney as a bodybuilder and as a man.

Mike Myers was at World Gym the first time Lee trained there, and he watched as Eddie Giuliani told Joe Gold to come out of the office to see this incredible kid. Joe looked at Lee and asked him to raise his pants because he wanted to see his calf muscle. When he saw it, he predicted that Lee would become a champion bodybuilder because his calves were as muscular as his upper body.

**Mike Mentzer**

During my time at Gold's Gym, I met Mike Mentzer and was always impressed by his solid physique. I also admired him for challenging conventional wisdom. He said you don't need to spend two hours in the gym every day to build big muscles; you can build them by short workouts, one or two sets per body part, with maximum effort. He called it "heavy-duty training."

He gave the example of getting a suntan and pointed out that if a sunbather went out for a half-hour when the sun was hottest, he would get tan. Immediately, I thought, yes, but if a sunbather spent all day in the sun, including when it was hottest, he would get more tan.

Knowing what I know now about the importance of enjoying your workouts, I can't think of anything more unenjoyable than that type of high intensity training, so it is not for me. I prefer to start with lighter weights and gradually work up to a high intensity set, while heavy-duty training advocates one or two warm-ups and then a set working to your max. But still, Mike Mentzer was thoughtful and willing to question everything, which I admire.

Samir Bannout was another Mr. Olympia winner who trained at World. He was giant year-round. I would always say hello to him, and he was friendly in return. But after Mike and I started training with Bertil Fox, who Samir beat when he won the 1983 Mr. Olympia, he was not as friendly. The audience made it a controversial decision by cheering for Bertil and booing when he was placed fifth, and Samir seemed defensive about his victory.

To me, all the guys at that level—Samir Bannout, Lee Haney, Frank Zane, Bertil Fox, and the others—were incredible. But after his win, Samir would walk by me and pretend I wasn't there. I actually understand that. He associated me with Bertil Fox. The truth is that I really admired Samir Bannout and thought he had an incredible build.

A number of professional athletes went to World Gym in those days. In addition to Kobe Bryant and Byron Scott, there was a former NBA star who became famous not for his basketball skills but for his right fist. That was Kermit Washington, who got into trouble with the NBA when he punched Rudy Tomjanovich in the face, broke his jaw, and nearly took off his head. Kermit apologized and said that he hit him because he thought Rudy was going to attack him.

What I remember about Kermit was that he was tall and strong. He and his wife came to World Gym often, and they really liked talking to Mike Myers. Kermit routinely did bench presses with 315 pounds for reps.

Besides Arnold, Franco, Lee, Bertil, and Samir, there were many other bodybuilding stars at World Gym when I trained there. I remember Frank Zane, Bob Paris, Chris Dickerson, Tom Platz, Dave Johns, Albert Beckles, Roger Callard, Greg DeFerro, Kal Szkalak, Tim Belknap, Lee Priest, and Lou Ferrigno, among others. The early female bodybuilders included Rachel McLish, Christine Zane, and Stacey Bentley.

Early one morning, I met the immortal Reg Park, who no doubt was in Los Angeles to see his son, Jon Jon Park. We were working out outside, and it was very cold, and we both laughed about how it was supposed to be warm in Southern California. He was a real gentleman.

**Reg Park**

Another celebrity who I met in the same outside portion of the gym was Sugar Ray Leonard. He kept to himself, as most people did, but since I had covered his first professional fight as a reporter in Baltimore fifteen years earlier, I could not help but introduce myself. His face really lit up when I told him I thought he was one of the greatest boxers of all time, and he was extremely friendly.

Other celebrities at World Gym in those days—either regulars or occasional visitors—included Clint Eastwood, Sylvester Stallone, Jamie Lee Curtis, Tommy Chong, Richard Jaeckel, Kurt Russell, David Lee Roth, Chuck Norris, Maria Shriver, and Patti Davis, daughter of President Ronald Reagan, who kept to herself and worked out very hard. There were many others.

But not everyone working out there was a celebrity or competitive bodybuilder. In fact, the vast majority of guys were just working out to get bigger and stronger, and gradually, more and more women joined to shape up, stay fit, and get stronger, too.

I am always proud to wear World Gym jackets and sweatshirts. I remember one incident, shortly after I had started Creators, when I was riding the shuttle at Dulles Airport in Washington, D.C., early on a Sunday morning after the National Cartoonists Society's Reuben Awards dinner. I was seated across from Jean and Charles Schulz. His nickname was Sparky, and he was the creator of the comic strip *Peanuts*. Sparky noticed the World Gym insignia on my jacket and asked me about it. I told him that it was a great gym, and he said he was building his own home gym and was really interested in the subject.

A few years later, *Forbes* magazine reported that Charles Schulz was the highest paid entertainer in the world, making something like a million dollars a week, mainly from Snoopy licensing, year after year. I really liked Sparky, and when I read that, I wondered how his workouts were coming. Sparky understood that no matter how rich he was, he still had to exercise himself. He couldn't pay someone to do it for him. I asked him later about his workouts, and he said they were fine but that his real passion was ice hockey. Whatever physical activity you enjoy that keeps you fit—that's the best workout for you.

I am so grateful to have been at the original World Gym and Gold's Gym, which were the flagships for the hundreds of World and Gold's gyms worldwide. I am grateful to all the people who trained hard and inspired me to do the same. As I look back, the environment at those gyms was one of the main reasons that I succeeded in sticking with a program of lifting weights. If you have been working out for a long time, then you have no doubt found a gym that you like. If you are just starting out or want to get back into shape, choosing the right gym for you can be the difference between success and failure.

CHAPTER TWENTY FOUR

~ ~ ~ ~ ~

# ENJOYING LIFTING WEIGHTS

I mentioned my brother John, who trained with Mike Myers and me from 2000 until 2003. We would work out together at our office gym in the late afternoon for an hour to an hour and a half, four days a week.

John is a runner, too, but when he discovered weight training in his forties, he started including barbells and dumbbells as part of his workout routine and is now very youthful in his sixties. John loves the feeling he gets from lifting weights, and he is convinced that it helps slow the aging process.

"I have been running every day for over forty years, since college, and still run every day and love it," he said. "I trained with weights for the first time in college, at DePaul in Chicago, but hated it and quit. It was not until I worked at Creators when Mike Myers was there, and the three of us worked out together, that I learned to appreciate the benefits of weight training."

He said that Mike offered a few simple tips that made all the difference:

**John Newcombe added lifting weights to his running routine and stays young in his sixties.**

- You don't need heavy weights to get the benefits.
- Form is more important than how much weight you lift.
- Even a twenty-minute workout can be enough.
- High reps help you get ripped.
- Diet is vital to weight training.

Those insights are very helpful when it comes to sticking with a program of lifting weights. The overall message is one of encouragement and support. Mike helped John feel good about himself in the gym when he was lifting weights.

Why did John hate lifting weights when he was in college and now loves lifting weights in his sixties? My initial assumption was that in college, he felt intimidated by young lifters who shouted and screamed at one another, trying to prove who was the strongest or who could make the most noise by dropping the heaviest weights on the floor. That is pretty typical gym behavior, and it is pretty awful. If you see that in a gym, try to ignore it or find another gym.

I asked John if that was the case, and he said no. The lifters in the gym at college were great guys and very helpful. He said he didn't like it because he didn't really understand it.

"It felt like drudgery," he said, "like I was doing chores—mowing the lawn or painting or cleaning gutters. It wasn't fun. It was boring."

With Mike's advice, the emphasis was on helping John feel good about his workouts—using whatever weight was comfortable and doing the exercises correctly so he would get the maximum benefit from them. Good form can take years of practice, and the benefits are enormous.

As for Mike's advice that "even a twenty-minute workout can be enough," his goal was to get John to go to the gym. We all tend to have an all-or-nothing attitude, and Mike understood that if John did not come to the gym at all, he would get zero benefit, but if he came for twenty minutes, he would at least get his circulation flowing and pump up his muscles a little. Most times, John would say, "This is kind of fun. I think I'll do some more."

At the same time, it is absolutely correct that a twenty-minute workout can be enough when you are pressed for time. It's not just that something is better than nothing; it's that something is a *whole lot better* than nothing. Over time, it can be the difference between being healthy and fit or unhealthy and out of shape.

Once John learned to do the exercises correctly and felt good about his workouts with weights, he started discovering benefits he had not expected. He sent me a note on this topic during the COVID-19 lockdown, saying he was impatient for his local World Gym to reopen:

"I did not realize how effective, helpful and good weightlifting has been for me until this last month and a half when I haven't been able to go to the gym. Even though I'm running every day, and walking in the afternoons, it's just not the same. I need resistance training. And it's far more beneficial than cardio and aerobic exercise. With this lockdown—the absence of being able to go to the gym has really proved to me just how invaluable weight training is."

John has stayed in touch with Mike over the years, and when he told Mike he really enjoys lifting weights, Mike told him he had been bitten by the "iron bug," which is a familiar term to those of us who love to lift weights.

If you are interested in starting a weight training program, my advice is to hire a personal trainer, but make sure it is someone who does not insist on a one-size-fits-all approach. You might need to interview more than one person in order to find a trainer who helps you discover your favorite exercise routine and encourages you to reach your goals.

My wife, Carole, hired a personal trainer for weights fifteen years ago. She said she wanted someone who devoted his life to training but felt that I was too close to home, in a manner of speaking. She had three sessions with him, pulled a shoulder muscle, and never went back. She has not lifted weights since—and her experience is not unusual.

I have a doctor friend who works out at a very popular gym in Los Angeles, and he told me he had met an older woman—she was eighty-four—who started working out with a trainer. The trainer had her do interval training and gave her lots of praise whenever she reached a goal. But not surprisingly, after a while, the elderly woman stopped coming to the gym. My friend said he felt relief that the woman had stopped doing those intense spurts of exertion. Being a doctor, he was always afraid she might have a heart attack.

The right trainer finds a balance between motivating you and not pushing you so hard that you give up.

We are all wired differently, and a good trainer can pick up on what you like best and what works best for you. For me, it is starting off by lifting light weights with strict form and gradually increasing the poundages, which I have been doing for many years. For you, it might be cycling or swimming or something else entirely.

If you enjoy your workouts, you'll keep doing them. It's really that simple.

CHAPTER TWENTY FIVE

~ ~ ~ ~ ~

# THE "BEST" WORKOUT

When I first started Creators Syndicate and was practically living on an airplane, my goal was to work out a minimum of four hours per week just to maintain the gains I had made over the previous decade. I boosted that number to six hours a week after Creators had become successful and I could integrate my bodybuilding workouts into a more normal lifestyle.

That goal of lifting weights for six hours a week has been my target for the past thirty years. That is a total of 312 hours every year. I still keep a journal for recording the body parts trained, the number of sets, and the length of time of each workout.

Now the six hours a week is an average. I'll take some weeks off altogether, such as when Carole and I travel overseas. We might do a lot of walking, which is great, but lifting weights is special. This means that some weeks, I will train more than six hours to make up for those weeks I take off.

To stick with a program like that—exercising 312 hours, year after year—is a special discipline that requires, more than anything else, *wanting* to exercise. That is the key to the advice Mike Myers gave John Newcombe. He helped him to enjoy his workouts so he would want to keep doing them.

When I don't feel like working out at all, I try a few different things to help me get motivated. One is to look for a book, magazine, video, or internet article about weight training that I find interesting. These usually inspire me to start a workout.

Another technique is to give myself permission to use light weights for the entire workout—no more than five- or ten-pound dumbbells. Invariably, after I start doing the exercises with the light weights, I want to start using heavier weights. So, I might do the first set of an exercise with five-pound dumbbells and then the second set with ten-pound dumbbells and then the third and fourth sets with my usual poundages. This is a great way to warm up the muscles to prevent injuries and to tease the mind into doing the workout in the first place.

**At age sixty-five in our office gym doing concentration curls in the early morning before work.**

I remember being surprised at a gym in the 1980s when I discovered some rubber coated plates that looked a lot like 45-pound Olympic plates but were only ten pounds. "Who would want these?" I scoffed.

Well, as I have gotten older, I learned the answer: "I would."

Sometime in the last five years, after I turned sixty-five, I bought some of these ten-pound plates, and I have found it motivational to use them. Of course, I know I am not as strong as I used to be, but I find it fun to pretend, and it keeps me coming back to the gym. For instance, when using 200 pounds for deadlifts, the bar looks pretty barren. But if I load the bar up with three of these ten-pound plates on each side, with five- or ten-pound plates sandwiched in between, it looks like I am deadlifting 400 pounds, when in reality, it is 200 pounds.

It might sound silly, but little tricks like this keep me motivated. I remember when a handyman was at our house and saw the bar in the photo above, and he said, "You can't lift that, can you?" I proceeded to show him a few easy reps. He thought I was Superman! Even after I told him about the rubber plates, he didn't care. He kept saying, "I had no idea you were so strong."

*I use these plates because my subconscious mind is saying the same thing in my self-talk.*

The photo of the Smith machine below shows a weight I was using for squats one day—100 pounds that look like 300 pounds. The result? Same thing. I felt stronger and wanted to come back for more.

**Tease your mind to make your workouts enjoyable so you will keep doing them**

When I think of working out, sometimes I think back to recess when I was in grade school. I'm not talking about phys ed class in high school, which most of us hated. I am talking about being in third grade and running on the playground with friends, kicking a ball or whatever, having fun and enjoying being able to leave the enclosed and stuffy classroom. If you think of your workouts that way, it will really help you to like them.

Over time, if you keep training consistently, you will start to see and feel the benefits. You will be able to eat more of your favorite foods, and you'll learn how to enjoy healthy foods; you'll sleep better; your doctor will ask you how you have improved your health; you'll have more energy; you will feel younger and more enthusiastic about life.

I remember once working out with a Mr. America contender, and we were both training very hard. This was thirty-five years ago. At one point, I went over to the drinking fountain to get some water, and he said, "You should never drink water during your workout. You lose your intensity. You've got to stay focused and suffer if you want to make gains."

Interestingly, I found out that he had stopped exercising altogether a few years after that. No wonder. What he offered was the worst possible advice for lifting weights—for finding a program that works for you, that you enjoy, and that you will stick with for years and years.

As we get older, I believe our focus should shift from, "No pain, no gain," to, **"THE BEST WORKOUT IS THE ONE YOU LIKE ENOUGH TO KEEP DOING IT."**

I made up that quote when we were on a family skiing trip in Canada. Our daughter, Sara, had just graduated from college and had hired a personal trainer for her workouts. We were in the hotel room, relaxing after skiing all day, and Sara said, "My trainer says the best workout is twenty minutes of stretching, twenty minutes of cardio, and twenty minutes of weights. You've been working out your whole life, Dad. Do you think he's right?"

I said that all three are good—stretching, cardio, and weights—but I had never thought about what constitutes the "best" workout. I mulled over the question as we kept talking. I thought about Sara's husband, Brian, who runs every morning; I thought about Sara, who loves yoga so much that she has qualified to be an instructor; I thought about Jack, who was really enjoying triathlons at the time; I thought about Carole, who was walking between two and four miles a day.

And then it occurred to me.

"The majority of people want to exercise but don't stick with it," I said. "Of the ones who do, what they have in common is that they *enjoy* their workouts. Either they enjoy the exercises themselves, or they enjoy the feelings and benefits exercise gives them—or, more likely, it is both. The more I think about it, Sara, I would say that *the best workout is the one you like enough to keep doing it.*"

This is the key to sticking with an exercise program to stay in shape for the rest of your life. For me, the best workout is some form of lifting weights—whether it was heavy weights with Bertil Fox, aimed at muscle building, or light and nonstop weight training, aimed at improving my cardiovascular health and flexibility.

This insight has led me to keep training year after year. I live one day at a time—and one workout at a time—and focus very little on meeting annual goals, but that's because I know that when I reach my goals today, tomorrow takes care of itself.

Lifting weights has enriched my life in all ways imaginable. As a result of my workouts, I have had plenty of energy over the years for family, business, travel, and all the other important ingredients of living a happy, fulfilling life. The fact that my family enjoys the benefits of exercise is a gift that I never take for granted.

I mentioned the workouts of each family member except Allison, who is Jack's wife. She is in great shape. I remember a few years ago when we were all at a dude ranch in California, and they had a giant, empty gym with yoga mats on the floor. Jack led us all in an exercise class, and I struggled to keep up, but Allison and Sara were hardly sweating at all.

**(L-R) Front row: Lillian and Scott. Back row: Allison, Warren, Jack, Sara, Carole, me, and Brian.**

Always remember that slogan for yourself: The best workout is the one you like enough to keep doing it. Do what you like best, and you will stick with it.

It's hard to believe, but it was more than twenty years ago when I made that discovery. Little did I know that it would be the theme of this book…or the story of my life.

CHAPTER TWENTY SIX

~~~~~

# RIC'S CORNER

One of the advantages of staying in touch with old friends from the gym is that they let me know what's going on in bodybuilding. A good example was the time Jack Yee sent me a link to a YouTube interview with Eddie Giuliani that was conducted at his house in Venice. I loved it!

I never knew Eddie well, even though we trained at World Gym at the same time for many years in the early morning hours. We both were there to work out, not socialize, so we really didn't talk much. I was excited to watch an interview with him at his house in Venice and to see what he was like while at home. I did not realize that he had become a millionaire by buying a house in Venice, living in it, and not selling it until many decades later.

It was the interviewer, Ric Drasin, who pointed this out. I discovered that this interview was part of a series called "Ric's Corner" that was very popular on YouTube. I watched other editions of "Ric's Corner" and was mesmerized by the host and by his guests.

He has interviewed Franco Columbu, Tom Platz, Robby Robinson, Doug Brignole, Steve Davis, Jerry Brainum, Boyer Coe, Samir Bannout, Reg Lewis (from the Rock Stonewall era), Leroy Colbert, Roger Callard, Jim Morris, Rick Valenti, Albert Beckles, Bill Grant, Denny Gable, Tony Pearson, Andreas Cahling, and many other bodybuilders.

**Doug Brignole was a frequent guest on "Ric's Corner" and offered a wealth of good information on how to train the right way. He was fifty-nine in the left photo.**
~~~~~

Ric also has great interviews with some of the men who made the business of bodybuilding possible, starting with Joe Weider. He has interviewed Pete Grymkowski, Ed Connors, and Tim Kimber, all three of whom built the Gold's Gym franchise, as well as Mike Uretz, who made the franchising of World Gym possible. I knew Mike from the gym and really liked him—a fellow Southern California transplant from Chicago.

**Mike Uretz**

Ric Drasin looked so familiar as I watched him interview Eddie Giuliani, yet I couldn't place him definitively. I sent him an email saying that I was intrigued by his YouTube channel. He replied and included his phone number, so I called, and we talked for an hour! It was a Saturday afternoon, and Carole was in Ireland, so it was the perfect time for me to get to know this guy. His knowledge of the "golden era of bodybuilding" was so impressive, and he was so engaging, that I asked if he would be interested in coming to Brentwood for lunch.

He agreed, and we met at A Votre Santé, which is a popular health food restaurant. I told him he was creating an audio and video history of bodybuilding that will be valuable for hundreds of years. He made a wisecrack. I can't remember what he said, but it was self-deprecating in a charming way.

**Ric Drasin in the 1980s**

When we had spoken on the phone, he told me he had written his memoir twenty years earlier but could not find a publisher. I read the manuscript and loved it. Creators Publishing released it on Kindle and other platforms.

The title of his book is *The Time of My Life,* which is fantastic because it is so accurate. Like Arnold, Ric was one of those people who learned to have fun as a bodybuilder. In fact, it is not at all surprising that Ric Drasin and Arnold Schwarzenegger were training partners at the original Gold's Gym in the 1960s.

In 2012, Ric received the first Joe Gold Lifetime Achievement Award at the World Gym International Convention in Las Vegas. He was the artist for the Gold's Gym logo, and he created the World Gym logo as well. These are two of the most recognizable images associated with lifting weights.

Ken Waller suggested drawing a Mr. Clean-type of figure lifting a barbell, and Ric, who loved to doodle, executed the drawing perfectly for Gold's Gym. And when Joe Gold started World Gym, he asked Ric to design the logo, and Ric created the gorilla sitting on the globe with a bent barbell in hand. You wouldn't believe how many millions of T-shirts, sweatshirts, and jackets have been sold with Ric's logos.

On a hot August afternoon in 2017, I drove from the Westside of Los Angeles to the San Fernando Valley to help promote Ric's book. I agreed to go on "Ric's Corner" so that I could interview him about his book. His recording studio was in his house.

Despite my best efforts, however, every time I would ask him about his life and his book, he turned it around and asked about World Gym in the 1980s. He was clearly more comfortable doing the interviewing, and he also knew a lot about World Gym from that time.

Ric was very close to Joe Gold, and he got a kick out of any stories I told about Joe. For instance, I told him how one week after I had prepaid for the year, Joe came up to me and asked in a loud voice that everyone in the small gym could hear, "Hey, did you pay?" I said, "Yes, I gave the check to Steve Merjanian," and he said, "Oh, yeah, that's right."

Then a character named Bugsy Siegel—yes, that was his name, and he even looked the part—came up to us and started comparing Joe to a landlord who hassles his tenants over every little thing. Then Joe said something back, and those guys went back and forth. It was good-natured but, for me, a little scary. Bugsy worked out with Jan Feldman in the early '80s, and they were both really friendly fellows. A few years after that incident, Bugsy had a stroke and died shortly thereafter—much too young.

**Bugsy Siegel of World Gym, not Las Vegas**

Ric called our segment—designed to promote HIS book—"Rick Newcombe, Publisher, Remembers Bodybuilding from the '80s."

I tell this story to illustrate how Ric Drasin's concern was with promoting bodybuilding. While we were being recorded, I could hear his phone ringing off the hook in another room because a famous bodybuilder had just died. His name was Rich Piana, and Ric says he was one of the nicest people you could ever meet.

Rich Piana was honest about taking huge quantities of steroids, human growth hormone, and other performance-enhancing drugs, starting when he was eighteen. Before he died of a heart attack at age forty-six, he had been put into a medically induced coma for two weeks.

Ric Drasin loved Rich Piana personally, but he was totally opposed to the ways in which chemicals have contaminated bodybuilding and weightlifting competitions. They have forced eager bodybuilders like Rich to take life-threatening substances, in life-threatening quantities, because it is the only way anyone can compete.

If you want to see the difference between natural health and fitness versus balloon-like muscles distorted by chemicals, study the photos comparing Charles Atlas—once known as "the world's most perfectly developed man"—with the ones of Rich Piana.

**Comparing the Charles Atlas physique with Rich Piana's: The "World's Most Perfectly Developed Man" 100 years ago and today.**

Compounding the tragedy is that I have no doubt Rich Piana trained as hard as anyone, if not harder. This makes it doubly sad. *Imagine pouring your heart and soul into exercise and diet in a way that, instead of adding thirty years to your life, robs you of thirty years of living.*

Ric Drasin has offered a keen insight into appraising current bodybuilders versus those of the past. He called it the "silhouette test," which means that if you were to see the silhouettes of John Grimek, Steve Stanko, Reg Park, and Steve Reeves, you would know immediately who was who. Even after relatively small amounts of steroids were introduced into bodybuilding, you could still tell the difference by their silhouettes.

For example, imagine silhouettes of Arnold, Franco, Frank Zane, Bill Pearl, Dave Draper, Lee Haney, and Larry Scott. I could tell immediately who was who. But if you look at the silhouettes of today's champion bodybuilders, many have a square look. Ric Drasin said they look like "a herd of elephants."

The problem with drug tests is that athletes can cheat and get away with it. The best example is Lance Armstrong, the world-famous cyclist who finally admitted that he took performance-enhancing drugs in all seven of his Tour de France victories, despite consistently testing negative for drugs.

Well, if Armstrong and other athletes can cheat the drug tests, so can bodybuilders. What is an honest promoter to do?

Why not have a silhouette test? That could work, where all the contestants whose silhouettes look the same, with the same square look, are disqualified, and all the contestants who are identifiable in silhouette by their symmetrical, proportionate, and *unique* display of muscles would be allowed to compete.

As part of his audio and video documentation of bodybuilding's history, Ric has presented some fantastic film clips of bodybuilders from the old days. My favorite is Groucho Marx's TV show, *You Bet Your Life*, where he had Joe Gold as a young man in the 1950s.

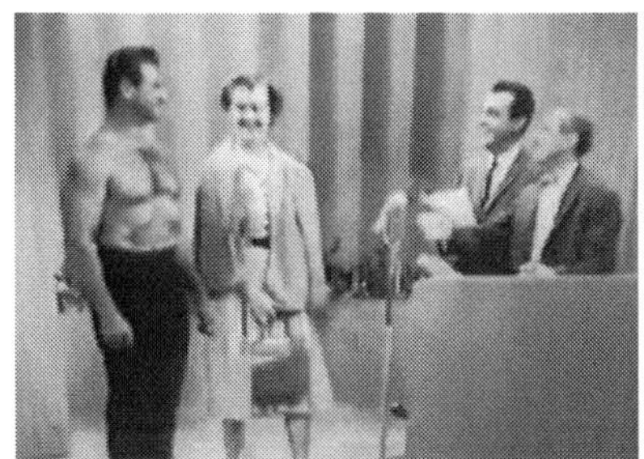

**Joe Gold on Groucho Marx's TV show, *You Bet Your Life*, in 1959.**

One of the things that made "Ric's Corner" so interesting was that he explored all topics even remotely related to bodybuilding, especially if they had to do with professional wrestling. That's because Ric himself was a professional wrestler for many years, known in the ring as "the Equalizer." It is not surprising that Stone Cold Steve Austin was a recurring guest on "Ric's Corner."

One time that Ric addressed an offbeat topic involved former Oklahoma City police officer Daniel Holtzclaw, who was wrongfully convicted, in my opinion, and who says that bodybuilding in prison is keeping him alive.

Creators Syndicate represents many political columnists, left and right, and conservative firebrand Michelle Malkin has been with us since 1999. She recorded a documentary on YouTube about the Holtzclaw case, and Michelle has convinced me of Holtzclaw's innocence. Michelle and her husband, Jesse Malkin, visit Daniel in prison, and he has put them on a serious weight training program.

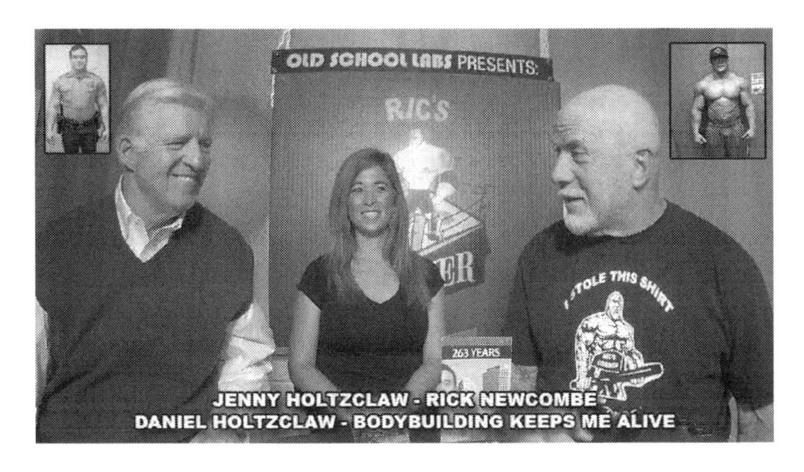

One day, I met Daniel's sister, Jennifer Holtzclaw, at Ric's recording studio to discuss his case on "Ric's Corner," and Ric was very perceptive in grasping what really happened and how this half-Asian bodybuilder was railroaded by Oklahoma City officials. The media presented it as a case of "Black versus white," so both groups—whites and Blacks—threw a half-Japanese bodybuilder under the bus and congratulated themselves on preventing a riot.

What made Ric Drasin so special was that he walked the walk, so to speak. He trained with weights since he was a teenager in 1962 up until his death in 2020. His YouTube interviews and commentaries are all interesting, and it is no surprise that he has 115,000 subscribers and 38 million followers.

One of the ways to keep training for thirty or forty years is to find books, magazines, and videos that inspire you to go to the gym. And there is none better for this purpose than "Ric's Corner."

CHAPTER TWENTY SEVEN

~ ~ ~ ~ ~

# USING PHOTOS TO STAY MOTIVATED

Bodybuilding is extremely visual, and it is no surprise that we measure progress through the mirror and with photographs. The mirrors in the gym and photographs of our muscles are the equivalent of stopwatches for runners and speedskaters or tape measures for broad jumpers and shot-putters.

Fortunately, I had a lot of photos taken as I was building my muscles. They are great to keep me motivated in my sixties and seventies.

What's even better has been the emergence of the internet—YouTube, eBay, and a dozen other services we never imagined thirty years ago. Did you know that you can buy muscle magazines from the old days on eBay? For me, they are wonderful motivators.

The current bodybuilding champions featured in the magazines have muscles that are beyond the grasp of nearly everyone. Compared with natural bodybuilders from a century ago, they look like they are from another planet. Drugs are the main reason why, and, like Zabo, I wish they had never been invented.

However, there are other reasons, besides drugs, why today's champions are so massive. We have learned so much more about good training techniques, working out, nutrition, rest, and a hundred other things that lead to a championship physique. You can take all the drugs in the world, but if you don't have the right genetics, you will not become Mr. Olympia. I learned from Bertil Fox how hard they train, and most people are not interested in that.

In bodybuilding, the ones who are genetically gifted will emerge on top. This is true in baseball, football, basketball, tennis, and every sport there is. Some people are better athletes than others. Of course, we can all make gains and improve our form in any sport.

But my frustration with bodybuilding today, and the reason I say it has become "contaminated by chemicals," is because the drugs have gotten out of control. If there were no drugs, the current champion bodybuilders would still be the champions, and they would be much bigger and stronger than the natural bodybuilders from a century ago. But they wouldn't look like a different species.

Once you see the natural strongmen from the old days and compare them with today's champions, you can see immediately that there have been dramatic changes because of chemicals. One of my favorite old-time bodybuilders was Sig Klein, who owned what looked like a wonderful gym in New York. He was strong, muscular, and super fit—a real inspiration to me to work hard in the gym.

I remember opening a magazine a while back and seeing a monster named Mike Matarazzo. He was a good-looking guy, with enormous muscles, and he was par for the course among elite bodybuilders—with a square, unbelievably thick look.

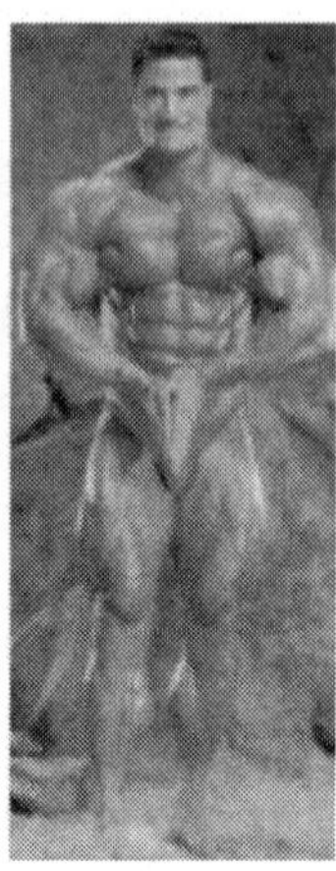

**Sig Klein** **Mike Matarazzo**

He looked like such a nice young man, and you cannot believe the amount of discipline and effort he must have exerted to build his physique. However, his overall size—like his competitors—was not something I could compare my progress with. I needed to find natural bodybuilders in order to have an apples-to-apples comparison.

Incidentally, I was not surprised to read later that Mike Matarazzo had died from a heart attack at age forty-eight. How many tragedies do we have to have before the hardcore fans of bodybuilding say, "Enough already"?

My heart goes out to Mike Matarazzo and his family, just as it does to Rich Piana and his family. These were such incredible bodybuilders. If they had been born a century earlier, they both would have been great strongmen of the era and might have lived into old age. This really is an issue of life or death.

The current bodybuilding magazines have great stories about training, diet, and nutrition, and some feature natural bodybuilders, which is fantastic. But I also enjoy seeing photos of natural bodybuilders from the old days, or bodybuilders who took only small amounts of steroids, like competitors in the 1960s, '70s, and early '80s.

I think it was the introduction of human growth hormone that changed bodybuilding more than anything. In the early 1980s, I had lunch with a world-famous powerlifter who told me he was experimenting with HGH. In those days, scientists were not mass-producing growth hormone synthetically. The HGH that this guy was ingesting came straight from the pituitary gland of a cadaver.

"I could feel my jaw growing last night," he said, laughing.

"Aren't you scared?" I asked.

"No, not at all," he said. "I know what I'm doing, and this will help me break the world record."

He did indeed break the world record, and that's great. I liked this man a lot and am not naming him or specifying the lift because it would be instantly recognizable. He is dead now, and I appreciated his honesty with me at the time.

Champion bodybuilders today must take huge quantities of steroids in combination with growth hormone if they want to be competitive. In addition, some take other drugs, such as insulin, plus diuretics. All of these drugs, taken in massive doses, have created a different look for musclemen. Franco Columbu says in his audiobook that the growth hormones make everything—muscles, organs, and everything else—grow to a disproportionate size. That is why Mr. Olympia competitors might have zero body fat but bloated bellies.

One day, I received an email from John Wood and his Oldtime Strongman website offering some bodybuilding magazines from the 1960s. I remembered those familiar *Iron Man* covers and found the magazines fascinating to read.

I started searching on eBay and found dozens more from the old days, including *Strength & Health*, *Muscle Builder & Power*, *Mr. America*, and *Muscular Development*. Another old favorite was *MuscleMag International*, published by Robert Kennedy of Canada. You'll find many inspiring photos and stories in these old publications, and they are all available on eBay.

I bought a bunch, and I'll flip through them periodically, especially when I am pedaling on a NordicTrack device during my workout. When I want to rest between sets, I pedal on this device, which has no resistance, and I find that it helps bring fluid to my knees. "Motion is lotion" is one of my favorite expressions. The more light exercising you do, the more fluid you bring to your joints.

Every so often, I'll find a photo in an old magazine that reminds me of one of my own bodybuilding photos, and I like to place them side by side, or one on top of the other, and then put them on the wall of my gym.

This gives me constant reinforcement of a feeling of success, which is essential to feeling good about training, so I keep working out week after week, year after year.

From vanity to good health—that is the progression. Most of us recoil at being called vain or narcissistic, but if, in our quest to look good, we use helpful tools that keep us exercising, then it is all good. That is why I surround myself with photos that make me look good so I keep going back to the gym—eagerly.

Yes, I am playing mind games, and I do them because they work. My gym is not "Rick's shrine," as one person joked when visiting it. It is a place where I separate from the world, go into my own mental zone of good feelings, and exercise for fun and good health.

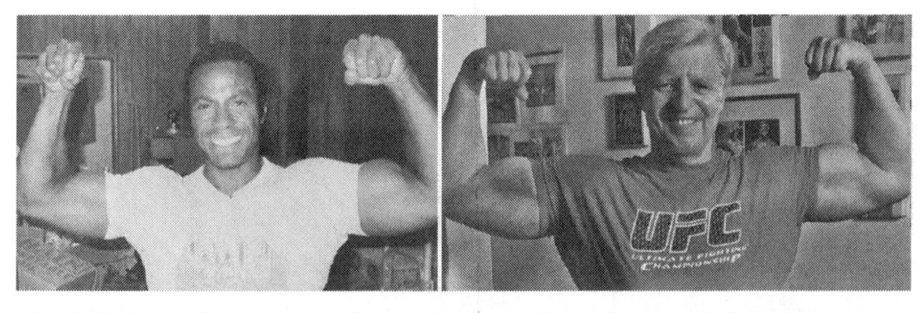


**The left photo shows Rock Stonewall at age forty-four, and the photo on the right was taken when I was sixty. It is amazing how important these types of photos have been to reinforcing my image as a bodybuilder over the years. They inspire me to keep training.**

One of my early heroes in bodybuilding was the great John Grimek. While reading one of the old bodybuilding magazines, I spotted a picture of Grimek that reminded me of a photo in my collection—in the same pose—so I put the two together and was thrilled that I looked as good as my hero. Of course, Grimek had way more muscle than I ever did, but when you find the right photo, you can look the same.

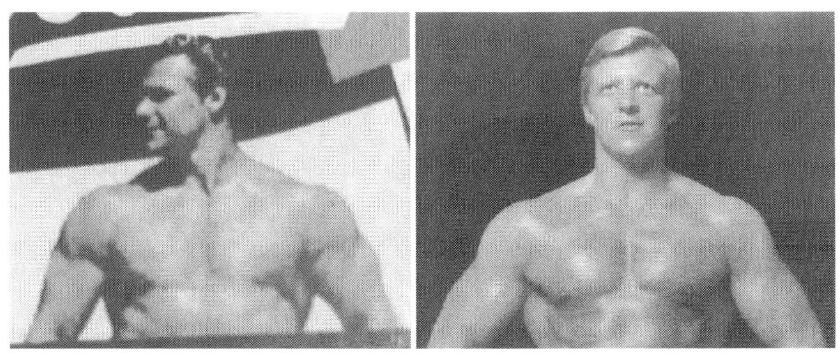

**Seeing these photos together of John Grimek and me really motivates me to keep training.**

**I always marvel at how aesthetically pleasing John Grimek's physique was.**

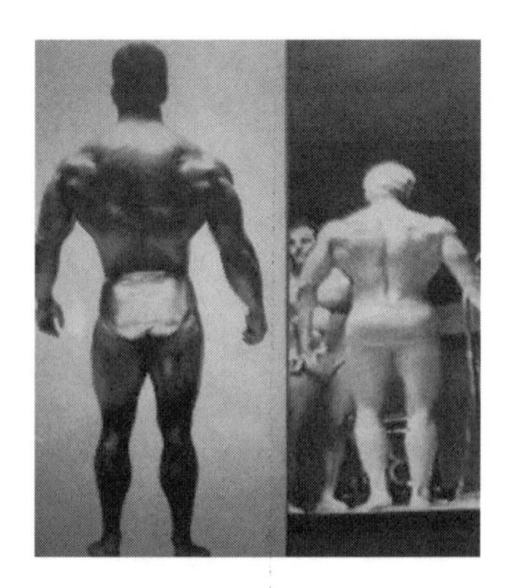

Along the same lines, I found a photo of my back from the Mr. Los Angeles contest in which I look similar to the giant Bill Pearl. Again, this photo was a fluke, as Pearl's physique was miles ahead of mine in all ways, but seeing these two photos side by side really boosts my confidence and motivates me to work out harder.

**It is hard to imagine a better build than Bill Pearl's.**

Not long ago, I was pedaling in my gym and looking at an old muscle magazine from the 1960s. There was a photo of Jack Delinger, Mr. America in 1949 and Mr. Universe in 1956. He was flexing his bicep, and I happened to look up and see a photo from the 1980s of me doing the same, so I put the two photos together as yet another motivator.

**Jack Delinger was always an inspiration to me in my early teens. Franco Columbu took the bottom photo. As he was taking the picture, he said, "You look so powerful!" That type of message is invaluable for success.**

I was never as well-developed as Jack Delinger, but in these photos, we happen to look comparable. This type of self-encouragement, which takes practice and a willingness to always look for the best in yourself, pays great dividends in terms of self-confidence as a bodybuilder, which keeps you going to the gym.

Something similar happened when I saw a bodybuilder on the cover of a *Mr. America* magazine from the 1950s doing a vacuum pose with his hands behind his head, and I remembered that I had a photo of myself that Bob Gardner took doing the same pose, so I put the two together.

**I have this photo on the wall of my gym as a motivator to keep training.**

Instead of displaying photos of what I want, which I put up when I was thirteen, I display photos of what I have achieved. This is an amazing tool for reinforcing my commitment to staying in shape. Too many bodybuilders reach their goals and then stop training. That defeats the whole purpose, which may begin with a desire for muscles but should end with health and fitness, which, in turn, helps us feel youthful in our golden years.

CHAPTER TWENTY EIGHT

~ ~ ~ ~ ~

# INJURIES

One of the reasons many bodybuilders stop training is because they suffer injuries, usually from bad form or too much weight. I have had pain in my elbows, knees, and lower back, and I found a cure thanks to Dr. John Sarno of New York. This is a man who Howard Stern says will be recognized as "the Steve Jobs of medicine" in future years, and I will explain how he helped cure me.

But before getting to that, I want to talk about shoulder injuries. I believe the biggest source of pain from decades of weightlifting is in the shoulders. It just goes with the territory.

Over the years, I have seen countless bodybuilders in the gym either quit working out altogether or succumb to shoulder surgery. There was a famous photo on the internet showing Arnold Schwarzenegger and Sylvester Stallone sharing a hospital room during their recoveries from the shoulder surgeries they had undergone.

Frank Zane writes about having shoulder replacement surgery. Dave Draper tells of his commitment to training after his shoulder surgery. When Lou Ferrigno paid tribute to Joe Weider at his memorial, Lou apologized that his arm was in a sling because he was recovering from rotator cuff surgery.

So many friends have told me they would have to lay off the weights for a while because they were going to have shoulder surgery. I had heard and read about many different theories for the cause of this problem. The most common explanation was worn-out cartilage.

My first encounter with shoulder pain occurred when I was fifty. It was my right shoulder, and the pain was very severe, forcing me to use light weights. I did a ton of high-rep shoulder exercises using two- and three-pound dumbbells. The pain finally subsided after three months.

Then, five years later, the pain came back with a vengeance. Wow, did that hurt! I could not lift a bar off a bench for bench presses because it felt as if someone were driving a nail through my right shoulder. I dealt with it by doing sets of fifty and one hundred reps of extremely light-weighted or freehand physical therapy movements. I could still work my legs, abs, and back, but that's it. No shoulders, chest, or arms, because my right shoulder was in some way involved with every exercise.

I tried alternative treatments, such as acupuncture and Chinese medicine, but to no avail. I found the best treatment was time and rest, and a year and a half later, I was finally able to resume my normal workout routine.

But it wasn't quite normal, because I was secretly dreading another injury to that same shoulder. Consequently, I would not work out as hard as I did before. And then it came, one month before my sixtieth birthday. I was climbing into the driver's seat of my car, holding a heavy briefcase horizontally in my right hand. As I sat down and simultaneously laid the briefcase flat on the passenger seat, I heard something go, POP!

Oh, no! There goes my shoulder again! I couldn't believe it. Three times in ten years! I thought I would never get back to my workouts again. I felt all washed up. For years, my disciplined workouts had made me feel young for my age, and now I suddenly felt like an old man because I could hardly raise my right arm.

I saw an orthopedic surgeon, who said that I had a rotator cuff tear and was a candidate for shoulder surgery. I babied my right shoulder because it hurt so much, and I was living in a state of constant fear of damaging it more. I had won a contest in high school for doing seventy-five push-ups in one minute, and now I could not do a single push-up. I could not even do one on my knees; that's how bad my shoulder pain was.

During this time, I started reading everything I could find on the subject of shoulder injuries, and I discovered the book *Shoulder Pain? The Solution & Prevention* by Dr. John Kirsch, an orthopedic surgeon in Stevens Point, Wisconsin. My life changed.

What I loved about Dr. Kirsch's approach was that he was saying it was up to me to heal my shoulder—not some passive solution like lying unconscious on a hospital bed while a surgeon chipped away at my shoulder bone to create more room. Dr. Kirsch said that, by regular hanging, I could create the room between bones myself.

Initially, I found it difficult to hang with full body weight for more than ten seconds, but pretty quickly, ten seconds became twenty and then eventually thirty, which meant that I could hang from a bar comfortably for thirty seconds.

I corresponded almost immediately with Dr. Kirsch. He wrote out detailed instructions for the medical imaging lab to take CT scans of every nook and cranny of my shoulder. After he studied the results, he said my subacromial arch was curved more than was natural ("hooked" is the word he used) and, at times, was touching the rotator cuff, creating an impingement that feels like a pinched nerve.

Dr. Kirsch's advice was to keep hanging. He also encouraged me to talk to some of his patients, which was telling. It was amazing how they all got rid of their shoulder pain by hanging. But what struck me was how they succeeded in a relatively short period of time, with much less hanging than I was doing.

Initially, Dr. Kirsch could not explain this, and he said he was frustrated because I was doing so much hanging and the impingement was still there, though there was slight improvement.

Then, one night, just before going to bed, an idea flashed into his head, and he raced to his computer and sent me an email in red type saying: ***"You have been a heavy weight lifter for all these years and your skeletal structures are massive in comparison with folks who seldom lift more than groceries. Your X-ray studies confirm this: You have strong, solid, hard bone, and your CA arch is certain to be very rigid. So there it is: the answer! And it ... will ... simply ... take ... more ... TIME for gravity to bend your CA arch and for Wolff's law to act. You are doing it right, doing a lot of hanging from your bar."***

**When I hang, I either use a wide grip, as in this photo, or a more narrow grip, roughly six to eight inches apart.**

Well, that is what I did, and my shoulder kept getting better and better. Within a year, I was pretty much back to normal, and I have been hanging ever since. I start most of my workouts with three sets of one-minute partial hangs, which means I keep my feet on a bench, though I use full body weight for ten- to fifteen-second spurts throughout the exercises. When I put my feet on the bench, I make sure to feel the pressure of my weight on the right shoulder. I do supersets of the three light exercises outlined in the book, only I use light Indian clubs instead of dumbbells.

Sometimes, I will hang with full body weight for one minute, just to test myself. When I hang with full body weight, with my feet several inches off the ground, I visualize my CA arch straightening out, which creates space between the CA arch and rotator cuff.

There are other benefits from hanging, such as improved posture, better balance, and relief of pressure on the lower back. I don't mind the calluses on my hands, but if you do, you can always wear weightlifting gloves.

One of the health benefits of lifting weights is that our bone density increases—at least, that's the theory. I found it encouraging to read Dr. Kirsch's analysis in red italics, where he said that all those weights I had lifted over the years left me with "strong, solid, hard bone" that was visible on the CT scan, which should be the goal for all of us. It was never my goal in the first place, but now that I'm seventy, I'll take it.

Besides shoulders, the most common injuries from lifting weights are felt in the knees, elbows, and lower back. I've had issues with all three.

When I was working out with Bertil Fox, the inside of my right elbow was always sore. I lived with it, and the pain went away after we stopped training together. I suspect I was using weights that were too heavy for me.

As for the lower back, in 2011, I got sciatica down my right leg and could hardly get out of bed for a month. The pain in my lower back and right leg was excruciating. I went to physical therapy and got some relief, but the real solution turned out to be from a controversial theory that my friend Bill McGowan told me about. I ordered the book that he recommended, *Healing Back Pain* by John Sarno, M.D.

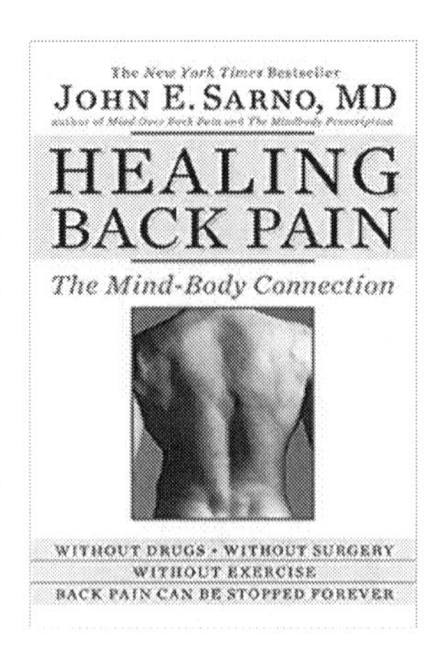


Dr. John Sarno of New York University said that many of us suffer from unexamined rage, which the body absorbs as tension myoneural syndrome, or TMS, which creates oxygen deprivation to the muscle. It starts in the mind, but the physical pain is very real.

I spent weeks reading all of Dr. Sarno's books, watching his lectures, and watching YouTube videos on the subject. Very gradually, the pain loosened up. That was nearly a decade ago, and my back has been in great shape ever since.

Howard Stern believes that John Sarno was an unrecognized genius who will be considered one of the greatest doctors who ever lived. I agree with him. And in case you are wondering why my back pain was so intense—what I was so angry about—I realized that this sciatica occurred several months after my mother had died, and there wasn't anything I could do about it.

In addition to Howard Stern, the comedian Larry David and the political commentator John Stossel (a Creators Syndicate columnist) both swear by Dr. Sarno. In all cases, they were in excruciating pain and were healed after studying Dr. Sarno. As Howard Stern says in his beautiful eulogy, which is on YouTube, he was terrified about getting back surgery—which all the doctors recommended. He avoided it with Dr. Sarno's advice and eventually became pain-free.

**This photo was taken from "Howard Stern's Eulogy to Dr. John Sarno," which is on YouTube. I highly recommend listening to it.**

You can't believe the number of times I have recommended Dr. Sarno to people with back pain.

But TMS can be very tricky. It can hide in plain sight. I say that because my right knee started to get sore when I was skiing a few years ago. I started doing half-squats and half-leg extensions, assuming my knee was damaged and wanting to shield it from further injury. My son, Jack, told me that he had a great physical therapist named David Fadale in Manhattan Beach. I saw David, and after he examined my knee, twisting it, having me bend in various positions, and doing all the things physical therapists do, he asked me if I had ever heard of Dr. John Sarno. I couldn't believe it!

"You're not telling me that this is TMS caused by unexamined rage, creating oxygen deprivation to the muscle?"

"That is exactly what I am telling you, and I am amazed that you really understand Sarno's theory."

From that day on, I started doing full squats and full leg extensions again. It took a few months for the oxygen to the muscle to get back to normal, but eventually, it did.

I'm not sure what the rage was from, but I don't care. I keep telling my knee that it is fine, and it is.

CHAPTER TWENTY NINE

~ ~ ~ ~ ~

# REUNITING WITH FRANCO

As the years passed, I stuck with my workouts out of habit more than anything else. Creators Syndicate faced the challenge of a dramatically changing newspaper landscape, and we set up a book publishing company, Creators Publishing, as a way to continue to grow the business.

It occurred to me that Franco Columbu's bodybuilding books from the 1970s had been bestsellers but were no longer in print. So I called Franco to set up a meeting at his office in Westwood. It reminded me of the old days, though it had been nearly forty years since I first went there. The office was only one block down the street from where his original office was. I do remember visiting Franco at a different office on Sepulveda Boulevard in the '80s, but his last office reminded me very much of his first.

After he showed me around, we walked across the street—a very busy street. It was called Westwood Boulevard, and most people would walk to the corner and wait for a green light. But not Franco. He just dashed out into the street, with me following, and we almost got killed in the process, with so many cars whizzing past us in both directions. Somehow, we made it and arrived safely at a nice Italian restaurant for lunch. He looked great and was excited at the prospect of republishing his work, especially as digital books.

We republished four titles, and I wrote a publisher's note that appears at the beginning of each one. The four books are *Winning Bodybuilding*, *Coming on Strong*, *Franco Columbu's Complete Book of Bodybuilding*, and *The Businessman's Minutes-a-Day Guide to Shaping Up*.

We also decided to create an audiobook of

*Winning Bodybuilding* because that book, first published in 1977, had sold half a million copies. Franco arrived at our offices in Hermosa Beach one day in November 2017 to begin the recording. We have a soundproof recording studio in our building specifically for audiobooks, and the audio engineer was all set.

But as Franco started to read the text, his accent became more pronounced, and it was difficult to understand him. So I suggested that I read some of the text and then ask Franco questions about what he meant, what was going on at that time, and what has changed since he wrote those words. My son, Jack, who is president of Creators Publishing, was in the studio with us, and Jack asked Franco questions as well. Jack particularly wanted to know about the old days training with Arnold.

The audiobook sounds like one long conversation with Franco Columbu, but if you listen to it while reading *Winning Bodybuilding*, you will see that we followed the complete text, paragraph by paragraph. We tried to change the title for the audiobook to *Conversations About Winning Bodybuilding*, but the algorithm at audible.com was set up so that we had to use the original book title.

We made the recordings over two days, and I was amazed at how much I learned, even though I had a pretty thorough knowledge of the subject before starting. Franco had such an intuitive feel for training, and he had so much experience, and his advice for bodybuilding was always among the very best.

**Franco recording *Winning Bodybuilding*.**

I have listened to this audiobook a dozen times, and he offers one training tip after another. It is incredible how much good advice is packed into six hours of recordings.

When Franco started lifting weights, he was a boxer and was told by his coach to stay away from weightlifting. This was not unusual at the time. The theory was that weightlifters and bodybuilders would become "muscle-bound," which means their muscles would become inelastic and they would lose their mobility. I remember being told the same thing in the early '60s. "You won't even be able to comb your hair," was a common refrain.

Franco said the whole concept of being "muscle-bound" is ridiculous. "There is 'fat-bound,'" he said. "Too many retired bodybuilders stop training but continue eating like they did when they were burning up tons of calories in the gym when training for Mr. Universe or whatever. They get fatter and fatter, and less mobile and flexible, and claim they are 'muscle-bound.'"

Franco grew up in Sardinia, with open fields and clear skies, where his most loyal companions were the sheep. He did not see a television until he was sixteen, and that was a small black and white TV in a bar in Germany. The first thing he saw on television was the boxer Emile Griffith fighting in Madison Square Garden, and Franco was inspired. He set a goal to have as much muscle as Griffith and to win a boxing contest in Madison Square Garden.

He talks about how he decided to give up boxing for bodybuilding, how he passed Griffith on the muscle front, and how he had a special feeling when he reached his goal—slightly modified, from boxing to bodybuilding—when he accepted the trophy for first prize at, of course, Madison Square Garden.

In the audiobook, Franco talks about the importance of giving yourself encouragement, and he cites this story as an example. It is okay to give yourself permission to modify your goals; what is most important is to feel good about whatever successes you achieve.

As Franco expanded beyond the text, Jack and I kept asking him questions about his training of celebrities, mainly because we were interested but also because we knew listeners would be interested, too. For instance, he tells the story about helping Sylvester Stallone get ripped for *Rambo II*, and he talks about being in Burt Reynolds's home gym with Reynolds and Jon Voight, who were training for the movie *Deliverance*.

Franco also tells some very funny stories about Arnold in his youth. For instance, when they shared an apartment in Santa Monica, Arnold always woke up first and wanted to go to the gym. But Franco wanted to sleep in a little, so Arnold would pick up one end of the bed and shake it up and down. Franco would get up, throw some raw eggs into the blender, and gulp it down as his wake-up drink. But after they were an hour into the workout, it was Franco who came alive and would challenge Arnold to "slap another 45 on each side of the bar."

Listening to the audiobook, you really get a feel for why they were ideal training partners and such good friends for so many years, going back to when they first met in Stuttgart, Germany, where Arnold won a bodybuilding contest on the same day that Franco won a powerlifting contest.

**After many hours in the recording studio, Jack and I showed Franco our office gym.**

The audiobook is selling well, and Franco was willing to promote it despite his busy schedule of seeing patients and traveling, both for business and pleasure. He went on Adam Carolla's very popular radio podcast, which was fascinating. He also agreed to be interviewed by Ric Drasin for "Ric's Corner."

I drove out to Ric's house so I could watch that interview in person. As I was pulling up, so was Franco, with a big cigar in his mouth! It was not lit, but he looked very relaxed. He said he had just come from Arnold's house, where they played chess and relaxed.

During the interview, Franco kept the cigar in his mouth or held it in his hand in full view of the camera. When there was a break, I suggested that he explain that he had just seen Arnold, and that's why he had the cigar.

Franco and Ric knew each other from those early days at the original Gold's Gym in the 1960s. At all times—when recording the audiobook and in all appearances to promote it—Franco seemed to be in great health.

So I was shocked when I received a text early one morning from Ric Drasin, less than two years later, saying that Franco had died in his native Sardinia. It turned out that Franco drowned while swimming at the beach in the Mediterranean Sea while visiting his family. He was seventy-eight.

Several months later, his best friend, Arnold Schwarzenegger, along with Franco's wife, Debbie, and daughter, Maria, put together a beautiful memorial service at St. Martin of Tours church, which was our local parish, followed by dinner at the Fairmont Hotel in Santa Monica. I wrote to Arnold volunteering to speak in honor of Franco, saying, "Franco Columbu changed my life."

I delivered the address and talked about how Franco was so charismatic and encouraging; he helped instill confidence in me that I had lacked from within, and I have been training my whole life as a result. I called him a "master motivator" and said that he was in heaven, giving us all encouragement to keep exercising. Arnold delivered a wonderful tribute to his best friend, and I could tell that he was deeply saddened by this sudden loss. He made a point of saying that, pound for pound, Franco was the strongest man who ever lived.

One of the highlights of the evening for me was meeting Franco's wife, Debbie, and seeing their daughter, Maria, who is a ballerina. Franco loved his family, and he told me many times that he and Debbie were close and how proud they were of Maria. Maria paid tribute to her father along with some of her lifelong friends from childhood, girls who had grown up in a three-block radius of one another in the neighborhood. The six girls, who were now young women, had flown in from all over the country to support their friend.

**Debbie and Franco**

**Ballerina Maria Columbu**

They had grown up together as sisters, from the time they were babies until college. All of them spent their childhood crawling all over Franco and proving how strong they were. They told stories about how wonderful Franco was to them over the years, and how much fun he was.

They went camping every year, traveling to the Drake family's lake cabin in Minnesota (Debbie's family) and to Sardinia (Franco's family). It is very unusual in Los Angeles to have so many childhood friends who stay in close contact as adults despite living all over the country. It was so wonderful that they all flew in to be with Maria.

**(L-R) Franco, Betty Weider, Debbie, and Maria**

I also really enjoyed meeting some of Debbie's brothers and sisters. She grew up in Minnesota and was one of seven children. One of Debbie's brothers was Colonel Mark Drake, chief of staff, 1st Theater Sustainment Command, United States Army. He was dressed in full military uniform for the services. He told the funniest story about first meeting Franco. Colonel Drake was something of a master at chess, but Franco didn't know that. So on a quiet afternoon when Franco was visiting their Minnesota home, Franco asked Mark if he knew how to play chess. Mark said he knew a little. Franco was excited and brought out the chessboard and proceeded to play, happy to help correct Mark when necessary. But no help was needed, and before long, Mark said, "Checkmate," and Franco was totally stunned. I think he figured out that Mark had played before.

After the memorial dinner ended and most people had left, I went up to Arnold and asked if Carole and I could have our picture taken with him, and he said yes, of course. It was very funny as we were starting to pose because Arnold poked my stomach and said, "Now remember what Franco always said about having your picture taken: 'Hold in your stomach!'"

**(L-R) Heather Milligan, Carole, me, and Arnold in October 2019 at the memorial dinner for Franco Columbu.**

As we were leaving, we met Jack LaLanne's widow, Elaine, and two of his sons, Jon and Dan. I told them that Franco always spoke highly of Jack LaLanne. He came from a generation before Franco, and he was the fitness guru for millions of Americans. They said they all loved Franco and were touched by the memorial.

That service—both at church and dinner—and Franco's death felt like the end of an era. While writing this chapter, I was looking through old photographs and saw this one of Franco with Joe Gold and Arnold, and I saved it because it was precisely how I remembered them from the early days at the original World Gym on Main Street.

As I try to figure out how I have managed to continue training for nearly forty years, hardly ever missing a workout, all I have to do is look at that photo. A good part of the reason was the inspiration, advice, and encouragement those three giants provided.

CHAPTER THIRTY

~~~~~

# STAYING YOUTHFUL

I started this book by telling you about a life-changing experience that occurred when I was only twelve years old. I am ending it as I celebrate my seventieth birthday, reflecting on the fact that the hobby of bodybuilding has added an extra dimension to my whole life.

Lifting weights helps me feel energetic and full of life. That is why I refer to it as magic; I was expecting one outcome, and then, out of nowhere, I got another. I started lifting weights to build muscles, which I did. But what about all those other benefits?

- Coping with stress
- Better sleep
- Better circulation
- Healthy eating
- Great lipid profile
- Healthy blood pressure
- High energy level
- Improved posture
- Increased bone density
- Better balance
- Positive self-image
- Overall feelings of happiness

I could go on and on. In fact, one of the reasons I wrote this book was to keep myself motivated to train throughout the next decade by reminding myself of all these benefits. All of the tips for staying motivated to keep lifting weights came from my personal experience, and I hope you are able to use some of them for your own workouts.

Once you get bitten by the "iron bug," you will know what I am talking about. You just feel so good all the time! Others have called barbells "iron pills," and the term "pumping iron" became ubiquitous after the book and movie of the same name.

I'm not offering a training or dietary program because there are so many good ones available, and the point of this book is to persuade
~~~~~

you to lift weights in whatever way is best for you—so that you'll keep at it.

By telling you my story and sharing some of the secrets that have worked for me as motivators, I hope to help you start or stick with an exercise program that includes lifting weights with good form.

Finding this "fountain of youth" was never my goal, but I feel like that is what I have discovered. Or, more precisely, what I have discovered is the "foundation for energy" as a senior citizen, which makes everything else possible.

It is not youth, per se, that I am after, and there are many things involving aging that weights won't help with a bit. For instance, lifting weights will not improve your eyesight or hearing; it won't prevent sun spots; it won't help your teeth or dental work; it won't prevent you from going bald; and it doesn't do a thing for all those other aspects of aging over which we have little or no control.

Can you believe that I got shingles in the eye when I was writing this chapter? That is amazingly painful and usually caused by stress. I wish I had gotten the shingles vaccine, and I plan to get it once my eye is fully healed. My point is that weights provide a million benefits, but still, they are no substitute for good medical care.

**Jack LaLanne**

The primary benefit that a program of lifting weights provides is to help you *feel* younger. Remember, too, that aging is a good thing, considering the alternative. Few people have aged more gracefully than Jack LaLanne, who was full of energy right up until the end, when he died at age ninety-six.

In recent years, a number of anti-aging clinics have sprouted up all over the country, especially in California and Florida. Many offer testosterone shots for men and small amounts of HGH for men and women to slow the aging process. These clinics are nearly all run by medical doctors, and I can understand their appeal. Given the choice, however, my preference is to go the Jack LaLanne route.

Just as Guy Mierczuk was my inspiration to build muscles, now it is Jack LaLanne who is my inspiration to live a long and healthy life, full of love and enthusiasm. Jack's positive attitude, which comes through on his videos on YouTube and in his books, is contagious and inspiring. I take many supplements that I buy from health food stores, but that's it. No medications unless I am sick, which is rare. I constantly work on thinking positive thoughts and on eating healthy foods.

It might sound corny, but the more you feel love in your heart—love for others and for yourself—the happier you will be. It might seem bizarre that after lifting weights for half a century, which is considered a macho endeavor, I would conclude that love, kindness, and gratitude—and, of course, grit—are the most important character traits for achieving health and happiness. I'm not sure if Jack LaLanne worded it that way, but that captures the essence of his powerful message. When we are grateful and filled up with love and good feelings, we can't help but be enthusiastic and excited about life, with a positive attitude.

Lifting weights is not a guarantee that you will live to be a hundred, though it does promote longevity. But many of the serious bodybuilders from my generation are either dead or infirm, mainly because they used performance-enhancing drugs. I remember being at a cocktail party where two famous bodybuilders were chatting, and I said hello and just listened in. They were swapping stories about their latest heart surgeries, and we were all around the same age. I was shocked.

I have walked down the street with famous retired bodybuilders and been frustrated that they had to go so slowly. I feel a real bounce in my step, just as I did when I was in my twenties and thirties, and it was painful for me to be with people my own age who walked as if they were my grandfather.

When I told Jack Yee about this, he made an interesting observation: If you were to walk down the street with NFL stars from that same era, they would be hobbling along as well.

In an earlier chapter, I mentioned my family physician, David Boska, M.D., and how I feel indebted to him. Starting at the age of forty, I would go once a year to his office for my annual physical. Each year, he suggested that I focus on lifting lighter weights, and it took a while for his message to sink in. The problem is that you need heavier weights to build muscle, and I didn't want to give that up. But eventually, when I was in my fifties, his message finally sunk in. Focusing on good form with light weights has helped me to enjoy my workouts more than ever.

**With Carole and David Boska, M.D., on my sixty-ninth birthday.**

Despite loving bodybuilding my whole life, I have very rarely gone to bodybuilding contests because I am turned off rather than inspired by all of the chemically created bodies. These contests are called "chemical warfare" for a reason.

Mike Myers and I have talked often about all those old champions who have died or who are in really poor health, usually after age fifty. Mike says, "I think guys have to make a decision about training: Either train like Bertil and do like he did, taking massive amounts of chemicals to compete in the Mr. Olympia, or do it the way we did, making training a lifelong endeavor to achieve health and fitness."

What lifting weights has done for me is to *slow down* the aging process, and I know it will do the same for you, just as it has for Mike.

**At age sixty-nine**

When people tell me they used to be bodybuilders, weightlifters, or powerlifters, I am always tempted to ask them what happened. Why did they give it up? Invariably, the answer is that it was too hard—too hard on the joints, too hard on the tendons; they had lost their flexibility.

That is why I recommend lighter weights with strict form, and making your workouts fun.

Body-building is mind-building. So much of whether you will work out depends on what you decide to do long before you go to the gym. But one of the things that will help you decide is to create your own home gym within your mind, where you focus solely on your own body—on your goals and, when exercising, on the muscles you are working.

At age seventy, I want to stay trim, though having a six-pack is no longer important to me. Being in shape and comfortable in my own skin are my top priorities.

Did you know that muscle weighs more than fat, so you could actually lose fat on a weight training program and gain muscle—and, consequently, gain weight on the scale? Your belt is looser, but you weigh more. That's actually a sign of progress. And don't forget, dense bones weigh more than toothpick bones.

Losing muscle mass goes with aging, but if you continue to lift weights, you can prevent much of that loss. Also, muscle is more efficient at burning calories than fat, which is yet another benefit of lifting weights. It means you can eat more. But don't go crazy.

Jack Yee and I were texting back and forth a few years ago, and he was working on his six-pack. I sent him a photo that showed me in my thirties with well-defined abdominal muscles, and he replied that I could recreate that look, which was true.

I replied, however, that this was no longer important to me. I sent him a photo from Thomas Jefferson's house, Monticello, showing Carole and me with two of our grandchildren, Scott and Lillian, and I texted him, "The whole point for me is to ENJOY LIFE, which means working out hard but also giving myself permission to have an ice cream cone with the kids."

Yes, I could deprive myself for a while and show my abs like that again, but I don't want to do that. For starters, I don't think it is healthy in your sixties and seventies, especially knowing that I would regain the weight later. I told Jack that I am happier today than I have ever been in my life, and chiseled abs don't have anything to do with it.

We all know that morbidly obese people suffer significant health ailments as they get older, assuming they do. But did you know that longevity studies show that people who are too thin also suffer serious health consequences? A small amount of fat can serve as a reserve against bacterial infection, among other things. A little padding helps if you fall, too, so you can avoid life-threatening fractures that are so much a part of life for seniors.

I always keep my body fat at between fifteen and eighteen percent. But I'm sure it was less than five percent when I had that photo taken with chiseled abs, and I don't think five percent is healthy for people in their seventies.

It is so much easier to stay in shape today than when I started training in 1963. In those days, you had to go to a health food store to find protein powder—always chalky—and any type of protein bar. Now both are everywhere, and they taste good. All airport gift shops offer various types of protein bars.

The same goes for gyms. Good gyms are everywhere today, while in those days, it was very difficult to find one.

Our politics today are disturbingly polarized, but when it comes to lifting weights, we all share the same values of fitness, strength, muscles, and good health. When I was in my twenties, there were very few news commentators or reporters who lifted weights, but today, it is not uncommon to find them. When you train a lot, you can tell instantly who lifts weights and who doesn't.

If you haven't exercised in a long time, you have no idea how much better you will feel if you start working out. I would recommend setting short-term goals, including a goal of six hours a week of working out. I picked that number for myself after training over a period of decades. For ten years, I exercised between eight and twelve hours a week; then I cut back to four hours a week for maintenance and then settled on six hours as just right for me. You can imagine how encouraged I was to discover that the same number is recommended in the bestselling book *Younger Next Year* by Chris Crowley and Henry S. Lodge, M.D.

I'm not sure how they derived their number—six hours a week of exercise, including lifting weights—but they say that this is, literally, just what the doctor ordered for people in middle age and older: "It's the foundation of positive brain chemistry. And it leads directly to the younger life we are promising, with its heightened immune system; its better sleep; its dramatic resistance to heart attack, stroke, hypertension, Alzheimer's disease, arthritis, diabetes, high cholesterol and depression. All that comes from exercise."

Remember, your workouts should not be crazy or painful—just moderate exercise with light dumbbells and barbells, and very little rest between exercises: light weights, good form, and little to no rest between exercises should do the trick. Or you could spend time on any number of the dozens of exercise machines that have been invented in recent years.

The main point to remember is that the best workout is the one you like enough to keep doing it. If you say, "Oh, I don't have that kind of time," think about all the great world leaders, whether in politics or business, who make exercise a priority. Presidents Jimmy Carter, Ronald Reagan, George H.W. Bush, Bill Clinton, George W. Bush, and Barack Obama all made time for working out despite the incredible demands of their schedules. Same with Jeff Bezos of Amazon, Tim Cook of Apple, and Jack Dorsey of Twitter. Then there is the energetic Mark Cuban and the indefatigable Rupert Murdoch, both of whom stay in great shape through regular exercise. Many successful female leaders, such as Michelle Obama, also make working out a priority in their daily schedules.

**Bill Clinton**

**George W. Bush**

**Barack and Michelle Obama**

**Ronald Reagan**

**Jeff Bezos**

**Tim Cook**

Of course, not all business or political leaders exercise, and some of them, such as President Donald Trump, clearly have no shortage of energy. But working out also helps us relax and ignore minor irritations. When he was first elected, Trump joked that his body was like a battery, with a limited life span, and he would prefer to work at being president than to work out at the gym. I get it, but I have no doubt that if he were to start working out, he would realize that his battery was being charged in unimaginable ways, and he would just feel so invigorated. Same with Warren Buffett, a man in his nineties who brags about loving junk food.

One of the reasons I mention all these business and political leaders who work out is to point out that if they can find the time to exercise, so can you. But another reason is to highlight the fact that staying in shape is one hundred percent within your control. Despite all his wealth, Jeff Bezos can't pay someone to work out for him. Amazon might have a million employees, but there is not a single one who can do a single exercise for Jeff Bezos. Barack Obama could not set up a presidential commission to do the reps for him. Each of us must discipline ourselves to work out. Nature gives us no other choice.

But there is something liberating in that concept. You are on equal footing with the most powerful people in the world when it comes to working out. They have to work at it just as hard as you do. If you start a business or run for political office, there is no guarantee that you will succeed. But if you start exercising and eating a healthy diet, there is an absolute guarantee that you will achieve results.

My advice is to start by setting your long-term goals—goals that inspire you—and then breaking those down into short-term goals that will help you feel proud of your progress. The beauty of healthy eating and exercise is that they always work. No matter what, you will make improvements. There is very little in life that offers us such complete and total control.

Finding the right personal trainer is one of the best investments you can make because it will pay dividends beyond what you can imagine. There are so many good trainers in gyms these days. If you keep looking, you can find one who understands that the best workout is the one you like enough to keep doing it. They can set up a program that you find enjoyable and refreshing.

Don't forget going for long walks, too. There is a famous walk in Spain and parts of France called Camino de Santiago, which is a 500-mile pilgrimage that starts in the Pyrenees Mountains and attracts people from all over the world. Many people walk some of the way each year for a number of years. This has always been a dream of Carole's, so we did some of the hardest parts of the walk, almost straight uphill, last year, and we plan to go back to continue our pilgrimage until, eventually, we arrive at the church of St. James. I did not need any special training for this. A lifetime of lifting weights, anaerobically and aerobically, has kept me in great shape for the walk.

**Camino de Santiago**

Dr. Hans Selye, an expert at stress management, once conducted an experiment by subjecting ten rats to the stress of loud sounds, glaring lights, and electric shocks. Within thirty days, all the rats died. So he tried the experiment again, only with ten rats that had been forced to undergo physical exercise, and all ten were fine despite being subjected to those sounds, lights, and shocks.

Exercising with weights makes you feel better in a million life-saving ways. It helps with clarity of thought. It improves your vigor and energy, and it makes you feel more youthful. There is no equivalent feeling to "the pump" that your muscles feel after a workout of lifting weights.

I wrote this book because I want you to succeed. I told the story of how lifting weights has enriched my life, and I have shared techniques for sticking with it—techniques that have worked for me and will work for you. Trust me, if I can do it, you can, too.

You will marvel at your newfound energy and stamina, and you won't believe how much better you will feel. You will have discovered magic—the magic of lifting weights.

# ACKNOWLEDGMENTS AND CREDITS

I started writing this book in 2015, jotting down a few thoughts and gathering photographs from my early bodybuilding days, but I did not pursue it as a full-time project because I was too busy with work, travel, working out, and other time-consuming activities.

Then came the lockdown in 2020, when most employees at Creators were working from home, and our communication was primarily through Zoom conference calls. I decided it was an ideal time to write this book. The first person I contacted was Amy Wang, who was in the last quarter of her senior year at UCLA and who had been an intern at Creators. After Ty Romstadt showed me how to set up an outline in Google Docs, Amy and I worked together—always telecommuting and not once in person—to fill in the stories, lessons, and photographs that constitute the book. I am very grateful to her and could not have written it so effortlessly without her incredible technical help and support.

I am also grateful to Alessandra Caruso for her superb editing suggestions and for making sure my i's were dotted and t's crossed. Along the same lines, Marianne Sugawara found letters and photographs that I thought had been lost forever when our company moved from Los Angeles to nearby Hermosa Beach.

Another person I am grateful to is Sheila Telle, a Creators employee who walked past the office gym early one morning and poked her head in the door to say, "Happy birthday!" on my 68th birthday, and I said, "Happy birthday!" in reply; Sheila is younger than me, but we were both born on August 8. I asked her if she would mind snapping a photo of me flexing my arms, using my iPhone. I liked the picture and put it on the cover. I want to thank Pete Kaminski for his creative design of the front and back covers. I also want to thank the Seattle City Council, Austin Community College, and the Ronald Reagan Presidential Library for the photos of Jeff Bezos, Tim Cook, and Ronald Reagan, respectively.

Finally, I want to thank the millions of people who are devoting their lives to health and fitness through exercise and proper nutrition. The explosion of great workout programs and fantastic advice for staying in shape has improved the quality of all of our lives immeasurably.

# AFTERWORD

The reaction to this book has been encouraging and heartfelt. Many readers have told me of their own similar personal stories, and others, who are just starting to exercise, have said that I struck a chord with them. One of the most enthusiastic notes came from Charles Gaines, who popularized the term "pumping iron." The opening line of Charles's note kept me going for months: "Man, I LOVED your book!"

*The Daily Caller* ran a headline about the book, "Cultivating a Passion," which is a great summary of my philosophy of life. The review quotes me as saying that the most important thing is to create your own unique, individual life.

John Newcombe is a professional filmmaker, and he made a wonderful twenty-four-minute movie about the book that is on YouTube called "A Bodybuilder for Life." John Hansen and Dave Palumbo are both retired champion bodybuilders who offer videos and podcasts similar to "Ric's Corner," and they understand the benefits of weight training. You can find their lengthy interviews with me discussing *The Magic of Lifting Weights* online.

Since this book was published, I have noticed that the theme of *enjoying your exercise* is everywhere. I have been reading about fitness for sixty years, and I don't ever remember seeing this theme advocated as being the most important, until now. Was it because of this book? I don't know. I just know that more and more "experts" are becoming aware of it.

Six months after the book was published, during the summer of 2021, *The New York Times* reported on numerous studies from universities that showed multiple benefits from lifting weights. My favorite was the study of fat and muscle, which concluded that muscle molecules squeeze out fat molecules. That explains why the bodybuilders who continued to lift light weights with good form, such as Zabo Koszewski and Eddie Giuliani, stayed lean, youthful, and energetic into old age.

Here are some of the people I remember from World Gym and Gold's Gym, all of whom have been lifting weights for more than forty years and look and feel youthful in their sixties and seventies as a result of a lifetime of training. These photos were taken in 2021.

**(L-R) Tom Marcoccia, Jim Gisondo, me, Doug Brignole, and Don Trepany.**

**I am surrounded by Ed Connors (left) and Marc Martinez. Ed's book, *The Three Muscleteers*, tells the story of his building the Gold's Gym franchise with his two partners, and Marc's documentary, *Dream Big*, tells the story of Gold's Gym in the 1970s.**

# THE MAGIC OF LIFTING WEIGHTS

Made in United States
Orlando, FL
08 July 2022